A *Housefly* **Buzzes**
in the key of

F

Fascinating facts on all things flora and fauna

Written and Compiled by **Simon Nicholls**
Foreword by Sue Perkins

Illustrations by Jake Cook

BLINK
bringing you closer

First published in the UK by Blink Publishing
An imprint of The Zaffre Publishing Group
A Bonnier Books UK company
4th Floor, Victoria House,
Bloomsbury Square,
London, WC1B 4DA

Owned by Bonnier Books
Sveavägen 56, Stockholm, Sweden

Hardback – 9781788709194
Ebook – 9781788709200
Audio Digital Download – 9781788709217

A CIP catalogue of this book is available from the British Library.

Designed by Envy Design Ltd
Illustrations by Jake Cook
Tree ring illustrations © Shutterstock
Printed and bound by Clays Ltd, Elcograf S.p.A.

1 3 5 7 9 10 8 6 4 2

Main text by Simon Nicholls
Foreword by Sue Perkins

Blink Publishing is an imprint of Bonnier Books UK
www.bonnierbooks.co.uk

For my mum, Lizzie Corke, 1947–1995.
You taught me that any situation can be
conquered if you pull a silly face.

And for my partner Catherine,
the best funniest person I know.

Contents

Foreword

My childhood experiences with nature were somewhat limited. I grew up in Croydon in the 1970s, where 'green spaces' were the cracks in the pavement where the weeds poked through. My interactions with the animal kingdom were similarly restricted. The sum total of our household pets amounted to two gerbils – both of whom bred and ate with admirable ferocity. They departed this Earth after a mere three years, fat and exhausted, and were not replaced. Other than a brief holiday spent fostering our neighbour's dozy Samoyed dog and a hamster with elephantiasis of the testicles, that was it.

However small my window into the natural world might have been, I was nonetheless transfixed. Wandering through the small boulevard of stooping trees that boldly proclaimed itself as the local wood, I'd feel a sense of calm not normally afforded me by my skittish brain circuitry. I'd be delighted by the industrious thrum coming from the lavender when the bees arrived each year. I remember being six years old, gently unwinding a red admiral caught in the sticky skeins of a spider's web, and the pure delight as I set it free. And my dog. Don't get me started on my dog.

My eyes still prick at the memory of her cashmere-soft fur as she settled down for her very first night's sleep next to me.

It's no surprise then, that hosting BBC Radio 4's *Nature Table* is a complete joy. My role is a simple one. I relax back in my chair and am transported by our experts; taken across continents, through time and space, across sea, land and sky as they bring me wild and curious stories of this planet's riches. I've learned about gay albatrosses, parasitic wasps, and heard a truly incredible, albeit harrowing, tale of a drug-addled cicada whose bottom half was eaten away by an invasive fungus – but hey, he's too high to notice…

In between the laughter – and there is much laughter – there is awe. A reverence at the adaptability, complexity and ingenuity of species. Oftentimes, I find myself lost for words (a rarity, ask anyone), open-mouthed at the behaviours, tropes and, frankly, mating rituals of our plant and animal cohabitants. Often the things I learn are more astounding than anything you could dream up during even the most fecund of cheese-dreams.

This book is a celebration of these idiosyncrasies; a love story to all the diverse, bizarre, beautiful, shocking living things with which we share our planet. When you feel tired or that life has become humdrum, look no further than these pages to remind yourself of the magic all around us.

Now, more than ever, we should cherish our environment. All we need is a curious mind. From that comes everything that defines the very best of humanity – understanding and empathy. Right now, our planet needs us to have both: understanding *and* empathy. Let's stop destroying the very thing that sustains us. Let's love, honour and protect this precious, precious world.

Sue Perkins

Introduction

Hello. I'm Simon Nicholls: co-creator and producer of the BBC Radio 4 *Nature Table* series and writer/wrangler of this here book.

I thought it would be good to say hello and share some thoughts on *Nature Table* before we crack on.

The idea for *Nature Table* originally came from the brains of two people. The first is my partner, Catherine, who works for the RSPB. Catherine's a passionate knowledge on all things flora and fauna. The second brain belongs to the chump writing this, me. I've been a comedy producer for the past 20-ish years, mostly at the BBC. Catherine's great passion and knowledge for wildlife has been passed on to me. And we're lucky to live in Penzance, Cornwall, where we regularly go for walks along coastal paths, spotting flora and fauna.

I've always enjoyed making comedy shows that take a subject that isn't an obvious fit for comedy, and showing it off in a surprising new light. As Catherine and I sat in many a pub after many a long countryside walk (there's a pattern here), it became clear to us that there could be a new way of celebrating the natural world, by showing off its quirky, entertaining and intriguingly funny side.

For example, did you know that a cockroach can live for a week without its head, before dying of starvation? Or that the fingerprints of a koala are so indistinguishable from humans that they've occasionally been confused at a crime scene? Or indeed that some fruit bats perform oral sex to increase copulation time?

We realised that there were lots of entertaining natural history facts that didn't often feature on serious natural history programmes – facts that merited being shared with the world. And that's how the show came about: we wanted to celebrate nature in a way that informs, educates and is funny. Thankfully Sue Perkins and Radio 4 were up for it, and here we are.

I find it funny that I've ended up making this show and writing this book. When I was at school I couldn't stand science; I couldn't connect with it. Science was taught in a very stuffy and boring way, using dryly written text books. Teachers would occasionally try to liven things up with videos of science programmes from the 1970s. These videos were very funny, but not in an inspiring way. More in a 'Check out how amazing the presenter's flares and sideburns are!' kind of way. Maybe making *Nature Table* is my reaction to that: wanting to celebrate interesting facts, but in a way that's memorable and funny (but without needing to reference flared trousers or sideburns).

Our aim with *Nature Table* has always been to inform the audience, to be smart but in a fun, playful way. All of us working on the show believe that if you can educate someone and make them giggle at the same time, that's going to stick.

So, this here book is a reportage of highlights from the shows, courtesy of our many superb expert guests (all of whom are named, so do check them out online), combined with my own personal research. Also featured are some of the excellent games and jokes from the shows: researched by ace Catherine (the RSPB one) and written by our genius writing team: Jon, Catherine (not the RSPB one), Kat, Jenny and Nicky.

I hope you enjoy this book and that it tells you some cool stuff you didn't know, elicits some laughs, a few guffaws and even a wry smile or three. The truth is, right now our natural world is being pummelled. Many people are fighting the important fight to protect and save it. But alongside saying, 'We need to act now, before it's too late,' I think it's crucial we remind people WHY this fight is so crucial. To remind everybody about all the wonderful amazing plants and animals we'll lose if we don't change our ways. I hope, in its small insignificant way, that's what the shows and this book will do: nudge us to remember and celebrate how brilliant (and at times amusing) the natural world really is.

Clearly a radio series and this book aren't going to bring about radical changes, but if we can at least engage people more with the natural world – giving them context for what's at stake, in an upbeat way – then that's got to be a positive.

WONDER WOMEN

The first *Nature Table* supergroup we're exploring is from the animal kingdom. I'm calling this group Wonder Women. It includes some of the most ingenious females among the world's glorious fauna.

Let's start with a wonder woman that's got real sass. She takes no nonsense and has some classy methods for getting her own way. No, it's not my Christian Dior-obsessed Aunt Maggie (love you Maggie). We're in fact talking about...

North American Dance Flies

North American dance flies are very tiny flies – only about 1cm long. When it comes to attracting a mate, these females are properly magnificent wonder women.

Dance flies are so-called because of their bobbing flight movements, which they do to grab the attention of potential mates in the swarm. Not to be confused with *Dancing on Ice* flies™, who wear sequinned jumpsuits, ice skates and love nothing more than moving to Maurice Ravel's *Boléro*.

Dance flies are also sometimes known as 'balloon flies'. This is because of their 'nuptial gifts' (a present that encourages a potential partner to become a definite partner). As leading entomologist Dr Karim Vahed informed us, the genius of female dance flies begins with these nuptial gifts...

Female dance flies never hunt for food
Female dance flies have no need to hunt for food, they're too clever for that! Instead, females force the males to bring them nuptial food gifts before they mate. Until the male offers the female a food gift, sex is off the table. Them's the breaks.

So, males are in the habit of catching an insect and feeding it to the female during copulation. All very romantic and recognisable to many couples across the species.

But a female dance fly's wonder woman skills go way beyond getting a free meal...
It turns out male dance flies prefer bigger, better-fed females to mate with. This is because larger females have more eggs and a greater scope for more offspring. As a result, smaller female dance flies have a wily ingenious trick for securing both a partner and free meal...

During courtship, smaller female dance flies trick males into thinking they're bigger than they really are to secure sex and a free food gift. The smaller females do this by having inflatable abdominal sacks, which they pump up before entering the mating swarm. By pumping up these sacks, a female fools the male into thinking she's bigger than she actually is. The old inflatable costume ploy.

★ **SUPER BONUS DANCE FLY FACT:**

Not only does the female wear her abdominal inflatable pants (available in all good chemists), but she also uses her extra-hairy legs to trick the male.

The wonder woman dance fly holds her super-hairy legs down the sides of her body to make her look even bigger. The male dance fly, duped by the inflatable pants and sizeable hairy legs, offers a food gift and mates with a female that appears to be large and fecund, but isn't. After copulation, the female deflates herself and the scam is complete!

Two can play that game

There's no denying that female dance flies are bona fide wonder women. However, when it comes to fooling the opposite sex, it's not all one-way traffic. As Karim went on to explain, male dance flies are cads...

Male dance flies always wrap the female's 'nuptial food gift' (often a dead fly). They wrap the gift by secreting silk from glands in their front legs. Silk wrapping paper, you say? Fancy!

But not everything is as it seems. Sometimes, a rascal male dance fly gift-wraps a flower petal or small piece of wood instead

of a juicy dead fly.
By the time the female has
realised she's been tricked,
they've already mated!
Two words for you:
Absolute. Scoundrel.
And even when a male
dance fly is honourable and
offers a dead fly to the female
as a nuptial gift, males will

often break off after sex and use the remains of the half-eaten gift
to attract a second female. It's like going on a date and offering a
half-eaten box of chocolates to a second date! Two more words for
you: Unbelievable. Cheapskate.

So, now you know about the outrageous deception that goes
on in dance fly courtship, how about we play a game exploring the
extreme lengths different animals go to, to secure a mate. That's
right, it's time for a quick round of **Fool for You.**

Fool for You is a role-play game. We're going to
try to woo you, animal-kingdom style. You have to
decide if these moves are genuine courting rituals
that help animals score in the natural world, or if
we've just made them up...

Scenario 1:   We're walking through the park. It's a beautiful day. I turn to you, raise my impressive crest, suddenly whip my tail against my body and waft chemical signals right at you. **Is that a real courtship ritual or are we making it up?**

ANSWER: **That's a real one. That ritual belongs to the 'smooth newt'.** Presumably named by someone who witnessed that smooth, smooth move.

Scenario 2:   I spot a love rival approaching us. Quick as a flash, I raise my wings out to their full span and start frantically regurgitating lunch on the love rival, whilst beating them with my feathers. **Is that a real courtship move or baloney?**

ANSWER: **That one is made up. Well, I think it is.** Who honestly remembers every night out they've ever had?

Scenario 3:   Bending down – bear with me – I start to build you a tower of sticks, decorated exclusively with blue objects. When the tower is finished, you inspect it and decide whether you're going to let me dance for you. My romantic chances now hinge entirely on this dance. **Real or not?**

ANSWER: **This one is real. Male bowerbirds build elaborate towers of sticks to impress females.** And, I imagine, they get extra points if they can skilfully remove the sticks, one by one, without the tower collapsing. Hours of romantic fun.

Scenario 4: I look warmly into your eyes as I lovingly offer you a wrapped-up piece of wood. **Real or not?**

ANSWER: **That's a real one. It's actually humans who do that.** Fifth anniversary: wood. Though by year five, I'm not sure how often it leads to mating.

Scenario 5: And finally: the sun begins to set gorgeously over the horizon. We'll both remember this moment for ever. I hand you a rodent impaled on a stick. **Real courtship move or not?**

ANSWER: **That's absolutely real!** The male great grey shrike will use thorns, sharp branches or bits of wire to impale their prey for mates. Though, to be fair, show me anyone who isn't wooed by the gift of a kebab and I'll show you a damned liar.

And that's the end of **Fool for You**. It's also the end of our look at wonder women dance flies. As both female and male dance flies demonstrate, nothing's fair in love and war. Now, I must go online and find myself a splendid pair of inflatable abdominal pants. Maybe in navy blue.

Orcas

Our second dazzling wonder woman of the animal kingdom is the orca. Before we focus on why they're such inspirational females, here are six initial orca facts for you, to get us started:

FACT 1: Despite humans regularly referring to orcas as 'killer whales', they're not whales – the orca is actually the largest member of the dolphin family.

FACT 2: Orcas can live in the wild anywhere between 50 and 90 years.

FACT 3: Orcas are in the public consciousness for starring in well-known Hollywood films such as *Free Willy* (1993) and also less well-known Hollywood films such as *Free Willy: Escape from Pirate's Cove* (2009, straight to video).

FACT 4: Male orcas typically range in length from 6–8m, whilst females are 5–7m.

FACT 5: Orcas can be found in most marine habitats around the world, from the Arctic to the tropics. Many believe that – after humans – orcas are the second-most wide-ranging mammal on planet Earth.

FACT 6: Some orcas migrate huge distances. Antarctic orcas have been tracked doing a non-stop roundtrip of 5,840 miles (5,398km) to subtropical waters. Puts the 10k I jogged seven years ago into perspective.

Orcas are much maligned, and unfairly so

As I already mentioned, we regularly refer to orcas as 'killer whales', a title that's not just scientifically incorrect but also a label lacking in sophistication.

When we watch orcas on TV, the focus is often on the elaborate lengths they go to in hunting prey like seals and whales. Tense, dramatic music always accompanies the footage, reminding the audience that the orcas are the baddies.

It's true that orcas are super-intelligent, skilled, apex predators. No one is denying that. But there's so much more to them than this. Thankfully, ace zoologist and broadcaster Lucy Cooke joined us on the show. Lucy has studied orcas up close and she painted a far more nuanced, eye-opening and positive picture of these remarkable mammals...

Orcas are all about family

What makes orcas so inspirational – in a way that we humans could learn from – is their complex societies. Only elephants and higher primates have comparably complex social structures.

Orcas live in families (pods) all their lives. Male and female offspring never leave their mothers (though males will mate with females in other pods, always returning to live with their mother and other family members).

For many years, we wrongly assumed that male orcas were in charge, leading their family's pod. We now know this isn't true. Not only do female orcas lead the family, but it's the post-menopausal grandmothers who are in control. Power to the post-menopausal Granny Orca Wonder Women! BOOM!

Tell us more about these post-menopausal wonder women

The menopause is rare amongst mammals... only humans, orcas and pilot whales experience it. These three different mammals all share a relatively long lifespan – with mothers living long enough to be alongside their daughters. Scientists believe that the older females have evolved to forfeit their own ability to reproduce so they can support their daughters' offspring. The logic being that a young female's offspring are more likely to be healthy and survive.

Female orcas tend to stop reproducing when they're 40 (roughly halfway through their life). When they stop, their more fertile daughters carry on. At this point, the wise old ladies become the matriarch leaders of their group, getting overly involved in their offspring's wedding plans and regularly dropping unhelpful hints to their daughters about baby orcas.

The fact is, it's the post-menopausal females that keep their clan strong and alive. Not only do these matriarchs lead hunts to make sure the family is fed, but they also, as you're about to discover, show great empathy for one another. What makes orcas truly stand out – beyond the cliché of being expert killers – are their phenomenal brains and emotional complexity.

Orcas have BIG brains!

An orca's brain is five times bigger than a human brain. Weighing in at 7kg, orca brains have more surface area for computational thought than any other animals on the planet. They have a remarkable photographic memory, remembering things from 25 years ago, like the first time they watched *Free Willy* on Blu-ray.

Orca brains have a paralimbic cortex. This is a group of inter-connecting brain structures involved with emotion processing, goal setting and self-control. We humans also have a limbic system, but the orca's is much more highly developed.

Neurobiologist Lori Marino discovered that an orca's limbic system is so large and complex that it has an extra paralimbic lobe (compared to a human brain). This extra lobe means orcas can process empathy and emotions – like joy, love and grief – in a far more advanced way than we humans can even begin to comprehend. To bring this to life, let me tell you about an orca called Tumbo.

Tumbo the orca

A perfect example of the orca's high levels of empathy can be seen in the true story of Tumbo, a Canadian orca, resident off southern Vancouver Island. Tumbo has scoliosis, which causes his spine to be curved and deformed. Scoliosis in an orca means their speed in the water is limited, which in turn affects their ability to hunt. For most animals in this situation, survival would be unlikely. But not Tumbo. Tumbo has the full support of his family, especially the pod's post-menopausal matriarch. Locals report regularly seeing Tumbo's family hunt and then swim over to share their food with Tumbo. And so we know for sure that orcas have compassion. They look out for each other. Thanks to his family, Tumbo is healthy.

I hope Tumbo's story shows you that there's so much more to orcas than them just being skilled hunters. I would suggest that orcas are a great example of nothing in life being black and white, but then some smart arse will point me towards a photo of an orca. I hope you know what I mean. Thanks to Lucy Cooke coming on the show and opening our eyes, I feel there's a case for us humans to try and develop our own extra paralimbic lobe and be a bit more orca.

Before we move on to our next wonder woman, let's play a quick game. As you now know, orca communities are led by post-menopausal grannies. But which other animals live in matriarchal societies? Let's play a quick round of our ratings-smash quiz, **Girls on Fire**.

We're going to name an animal and you have to guess whether the species has dominant females, or the same boring old patriarchy as us.

1. **Let's start with the clownfish. Is the clownfish living with a female-led matriarchy? Or a patriarchy?**

ANSWER: **Clownfish are a matriarchy!**
In the clownfish world, the largest, most aggressive female acts as the highest authority. The males serve her throughout her reign, and the one that pleases her the most gets to mate with her. This involves housekeeping, finding her a home and bringing her food. Luckily for me, I don't have gills...

2.   **What about spotted hyenas?**

ANSWER: **Spotted hyenas are a matriarchy.**
            The females have a large amount of
            natural testosterone and are often
            more dominant than the males. They
            also have an elongated clitoris known
            as a 'pseudo-penis'. The females will
            mount and attempt to mate with male
            hyenas, just to show dominance. They
            didn't put *that* in *The Lion King*...

3.   **And finally... What about the
            platypus? A duck-billed matriarchy?**

ANSWER: **That's actually a bit of a trick
            question.** Platypuses have no real
            hierarchy at all. In fact they spend
            most of their time alone, looking for
            food. I hear you, platypus. I hear you.

So, that's the end of the game and our look at wonder women orcas. I would ask if you had a whale of a time, but I won't because – as I hope you remember, orcas aren't whales: they're part of the oceanic dolphin family. Useful orca trivia there for any of you pub quiz fans.

Time now for our final wonder woman...

South American Giant Ants

The South American giant ant is – spoiler alert – a giant ant found in South America. Its habitat tends to be the rainforests of the Andes in Peru, Ecuador and Colombia. But these ants also live in the savannah and lowland rainforests of Brazil, Guyana, Bolivia, Paraguay and Argentina. Giant ants can reach a whopping – drum roll please – 3–4cm long. That may not immediately say 'giant' to you but let me tell you, in ant terms South American giant ants ARE HUGE! They're among the largest ants in the world.

> **BONUS GIANT ANT FACT:**
>
> Did you know giant ants possess a sting that causes severe pain to humans for up to 48 hours? So, don't be telling them they're small to their mandibles. You'll lose!

Female South American giant ants are serious wonder women

I'm not exaggerating when I say South American giant ants are badass. As the very marvellous Dr Claire Asher explained when she joined us on the show, South American giant ants have a mesmerising, female-led social structure...

One ant does not a colony make

You're probably aware that ants live in colonies, with a queen at the top of the hierarchy. Usually, the queen ant is the only female ant allowed to reproduce. However, South American giant ants are different. One might say they're more progressive...

Every giant female ant in the colony can reproduce. But to stop it being a free-for-all chaotic ant orgy in the nest (never thought I'd put those words together in a sentence), the females are organised and relatively polite to one another. The female ants maintain and respect the hierarchy, as they queue to decide who reproduces next!

Did somebody order a knuckle sandwich?

If I'm honest, saying that giant female ants queue 'relatively politely' for sex is stretching it. Fights among females often break out, as they squabble over their place in the queue. Research has shown that female giant ant fights often involve hitting each other in the crotch (not dissimilar to an *EastEnders* Christmas special, but with more ants).

To establish supremacy over one another, females also box each other around the head with their antennae. And if that's not enough to jump the queue, they do a thing called 'gaster rubbing'. This is where one female curls her abdomen round and rubs it on the antennae of another female – effectively playing a rudimentary game of Sniff My Crotch! Charmed, I'm sure.

Where are the male giant ants in all this?

The truth is, male giant ants don't live very long. Colonies produce males, the males mate with the females and then the males die. The process of mating actually kills the male, meaning the males are little more than walking sperm. Wham! Bam! Goodnight!

Giant ant mums do a thing called 'whatever I want'

Dr Claire Asher went on to explain that once a female giant ant has mated, her focus is on egg laying. Then, as soon as the offspring are born, they immediately become her worker ants! From that moment on, the adult female does nothing other than lay more eggs, whilst her kids do all the menial chores around the nest. Tasks like cleaning the oven, defrosting the freezer, defending the nest against predators and ironing mum's socks – that sort of thing. From the mother giant ant's perspective, the logic is: 'I've brought you into the world, now look after me!' I think I remember my grandmother saying something similar to my mother.

So, that's wonder women South American giant ants. Before we move on, how about we play a quick game of everybody's favourite quiz, **Ant or Not?**

Did you know that there are an estimated 22,000 species of ant? That's a lot of names to come up with. Many have been named after celebrities. For example, there's an ant called *Pheidole roosevelti*, named after US President Teddy Roosevelt.

Ant or Not is a very simple game. I'll give you the scientific name for an ant, and you have to decide if it's a real ant or a not real ant. Let's play...

1. Is this a real ant, named after a famous person: the *Pheidole harrisonfordi*?

ANSWER: **It's real. There is a Harrison Ford ant.** You can see it starring in *Indiana Jones and the Picnic of Doom.*

2. What about the *Sericomyrmex radioheadi*? **Ant or Not?**

ANSWER: **That's also a real ant.** It gets a bit angry if you keep asking it to play the song 'Creep'.

3. How about the *Pheidole freudi*? *After Sigmund Freud?* **Ant or Not?**

ANSWER: **It's not an ant.** There actually isn't an ant named after Sigmund Freud. But his name has been given to a penis. I mean beetle.

4. What about the *Doronomyrmex pocahontas* (try saying that with a Fruit Pastille in your mouth)? **Ant or Not?**

ANSWER: **It's an ant!** There is indeed an ant named after Pocahontas. A much better tribute to her than that film where she ended up with Mel Gibson.

5. And finally – what about the *Sericomyrmex sueperkinsi*? **Ant or Not?**

ANSWER: **Sadly, there's no organism yet named after national treasure Sue Perkins.** But if anyone reading this is working in an animal naming department, then we think Sue would suit a majestic leopard... though, to be honest, she's also told us she'd be happy with some sort of woodlouse.

So, that's our look at a few of the many wonder women of the animal kingdom. I hope you clearly see that there's a lot more to the female of the species, than we may have previously been led to believe.

We will of course look at more amazing females across this book. It would be rude – and indeed foolish – not to.

BITESIZE NATURE TABLE

Before we check out our next *Nature Table* group, here are some juicy bitesize wildlife facts for you.

Did you know...?

Slugs have four noses.
So if you thought they couldn't get slimier,
now imagine them with a cold.

The ancient Egyptians referred to mushrooms
as the 'plant of immortality'. Stupid dead losers
got that one wrong.

A housefly buzzes in the key of F.
Though, if you ask one to do a verse of
Tracy Chapman's 'Fast Car', they'll need you to
provide an acoustic guitar.

The carnivorous cobra lily lures insects into its
pitcher trap, then confuses them with bright
luminescence and several false exits so they can't
get out. It's a method the lily borrowed from Ikea.

CHATTERBOX PLANTS

The next group of outrageous organisms we're looking at are Chatterbox Plants. People often think of flora as being boring. A plant is never going to be as thrilling as a rhino charging at you or two giant Galapagos turtles awkwardly having sex. But as we're going to show you now, plants are just as compelling as animals; they're just less showy-offy about it.

So why has the author (that's me) chosen the title, Chatterbox Plants? Don't panic, there's logic to this curious title. As we're about to reveal, plants are surprisingly talkative windbags...

Goldenrod

Originally native to North America and found in open areas, goldenrod is a herbaceous perennial plant. Considered by some as a weed, goldenrod is topped with beautiful fluffy yellow flowers and is an important foodplant for many species of moths and other insects.

Goldenrod has been cultivated in the UK since 1648 and was first recorded growing wild in England and Scotland in 1849.

BONUS GOLDENROD FACT:

Some studies have suggested that goldenrod can help reduce inflammation, relieve muscle spasms, fight infections and lower blood pressure. Goldenrod also has a history of being a traditional medicine, treating urinary tract inflammation and treating kidney stones.

Gobby goldenrods

As genius ethnobotanist James Wong shared with us on the show, what makes goldenrods so surprising, so interesting and so fabulous is their ingenious way of communicating. It all stems (sorry) from a fragrance...

Goldenrods don't have an aroma to us humans. But every goldenrod has a particular smell to other goldenrods. Research has shown that goldenrods communicate with other goldenrods. They can send out a variety of messages by emitting different chemical scents. The smells are like smoke signals, coming from the goldenrod's leaves.

Other plants also pick up the goldenrods' fragrant messages. This means that when a goldenrod is attacked, it can let other plants know what's going on. It's as if goldenrods have a family WhatsApp group where they can communicate with other goldenrods. But via their smell-based WhatsApp, goldenrods can also communicate with the massive chat group of all the other plants (though goldenrods normally stick to chatting with their own kind, as they generally don't want other plants benefitting from their intel!).

Plants tend only to speak to other groups of plants when there's a real life-and-death emergency (similar to the relationship many of us have with our next door neighbours). So, even for plants, information is power!

But it's not just goldenrods that can communicate through smells. James Wong explained that other plants get in on the game too...

Many of us love the smell of a freshly cut lawn in the summer. It's a very particular smell. But did you know that the distinctive scent of freshly cut grass is actually the grass sending out distress signals to other plants? When threatened, grass is even known to give off hormones that attract wasps. This is beneficial to the grass because wasps will defend the grass against grass-eating insects. Grass is calling in the cavalry! Still think plants are boring?!

> ## BONUS CHATTERBOX PLANT FACT:
> Studies have demonstrated that as well as being able to communicate, plants also have regional accents! As James Wong told us, Northern Californian sage brush plants talk differently to Southern Californian 'valley girl' sage brush plants – it's like a weird plant remake of *Beverly Hills, 90210*! I assume all the characters drive around in their soft-top wheelbarrows.

So, hold the front page: plants talk to each other. It's truly amazing. Let's just hope that humans never learn how to communicate directly with plants. Or else the limp, sad flowers we bring home as a present will whisper, 'We come from a petrol station.'

Broccoli

Whilst we're talking 'talking plants', let's say a big 'Hi and hello!' to broccoli. That's right, our vegetable friend the broccoli is another chatterbox. But broccoli can go one step further than goldenrod: broccoli can talk directly to us! Don't roll your eyes: I'm not off my mash... talking broccoli is real.

I remember when we made the original try-out pilot episode of *Nature Table* for the BBC. The first item we discussed was a 15-million-year-old whale's ear bone, brought on by brilliant marine biologist Dr Helen Scales. The audience, Sue and the rest of the panel's jaws dropped at seeing something so incredible, so old and in such amazing condition (and with a cool story to tell). Our next item was brought on by the aforementioned legendary ethnobotanist James Wong. James opened a scruffy supermarket carrier bag and pulled out a floret of broccoli.

The juxtaposition of the ancient whale's ear bone with a chunk of broccoli got a big laugh from the audience. And that's what's fun about *Nature Table*: one minute you're discussing a mind-blowingly ancient sperm whale's ear bone, the next you're chatting about a stick of broccoli. But what made this moment so awesome was James telling us the incredible story of how broccoli communicates with humans. It still blows my mind to this day. So, let's hear what the broccoli has to say (sadly not in its own words) but courtesy of Mr James Wong…

Broccoli has been around for more than 2,000 years, and for many people it tastes like it. Many children (and quite a few adults) don't like the naturally bitter taste of this vegetable. We humans have evolved so our tastebuds find bitter things unpleasant. This links to the fact that bitterness, in the animal kingdom, is often a sign of toxicity. But is there more to the bitter taste of broccoli? Is the broccoli trying to tell us something? Indeed it is…

Broccoli self-defence

Here's a question I never thought I'd ask: 'How does broccoli protect itself?' I'm guessing that the best answer you can give is 'with difficulty', so here's the real answer…

If broccoli is attacked, it can't just run away or hit a predator on the head with a frying pan. To ward off predators, broccoli has to think outside the box. And when I say outside the box, I really mean it. That's right, broccoli uses chemical weapons to defend itself…

When a predator bites into broccoli, the plant immediately releases bitter toxins at the site of cellular damage. These bitter toxins act as a warning to the predator: keep eating me and you'll be poisoned. In theory, this is an ingenious defence mechanism. In reality, many of us keep chomping as we've evolved to enjoy the taste of broccoli (especially roasted with garlic and chillies). So whilst goldenrod uses smell to communicate with other plants, broccoli talks to us (and other predators) through specific flavours, created as it releases specific toxins. Clever, clever broccoli!

What's really cool (yes, broccoli is cool) is that these broccoli toxins – in our human bodies – actually have the opposite effect. Rather than poison us, the toxins help us! Our bodies react to the chemicals in broccoli that give it its toxicity and bitter flavour by ramping up the detoxification enzymes in our liver. So that means if you eat lots of broccoli[1], you'll need to drink significantly more coffee to get the same caffeine kick than if you didn't eat the broccoli.

The reason for this is that the broccoli we've eaten has improved and ramped up our body's detoxification process. So, ironically, the broccoli that's trying to poison us to protect itself, is actually giving us a superpower. So forget Spiderman, Black Widow or The Hulk – broccoli is where it's at if you fancy being the next Marvel superhero. Let me hear you make some noise for... Keith: the Super Broccoli!

---

1   On the show, James said 'lots'. We don't know how much 'lots' means, so best not to try this at home!

BONUS TALKING BROCCOLI FACT:

This form of communication – releasing flavours to ward off predators – isn't just seen in broccoli... our old friend garlic is exactly the same. It's only when you cut garlic that you get the intense garlic flavour. This distinctive flavour is garlic trying to ward off predators. The simple truth is, the more you try to damage a plant, the more it fights back with a taste we're not supposed to like. Eye of the Tiger plants!

Unfortunately for broccoli and garlic, as we humans become older many of us become less sensitive to – and in fact enjoy – the extreme flavours that garlic and broccoli produce.

So, now we know that broccoli has remarkable detoxification properties for us humans, how about we play a quick game, to find out what other plants can help us? Let's play a round of **BOTAN-A&E** (sorry).

In this game, we're going to role-play some scenarios, list some ailments and see if you can name the right plant to cure my illness.

Here's the first one...

1. **You're out on a hot summer's day walking with me, your best friend, in your garden. I get a bit burned from the sunshine. No need to call 999, but what plant or plants do you use?**

ANSWER: **Aloe vera and chamomile**
That's right! Using a combination of aloe vera and chamomile you're able to calm my burn right down. Studies show that aloe vera is anti-inflammatory, promoting circulation and inhibiting the growth of bacteria. Chamomile also has anti-inflammatory properties that help alleviate sunburn. Win-win!

Right, here's another...

2.   You're out walking in your garden,
      again with me, your best friend.
      Funny that. We've been on a bender
      (classic), we're feeling pretty
      hungover and I start to feel sick.
      There's no time to call an ambulance.
      What plant do you use?

ANSWER: **Ginger**
      Ginger will sort that nausea right out.
      It helps settle the stomach because it
      encourages efficient digestion, meaning
      food doesn't stay so long in the gut.
      Ginger is also a great carminative,
      meaning it helps to eliminate extra gas
      from the intestinal tract. Ginger nuts
      all round!

          People often recommend the hair
      of the dog for a hangover. It might just
      be me, but I can't think of anything I'd
      like to eat less.

OK, here's the last scenario...

3.   You're in your garden. I don't mean to
      be judgy, but you do seem to spend an
      inordinate amount of time out there.

I'm your best friend, so I feel I can say these things to you. Anyway, you're hosting a garden party when your best friend, that's me, has a serious case of itchy eyes and throat. I do a massive sneeze. Sounds like a classic bit of hay fever. You don't have any antihistamine to hand, so quick, which plant do you use?

ANSWER: **Nettles**

Yes, nettles made into a tea help soothe hay fever. It's thought to be able to reduce the amount of histamine in the body caused by allergies. Nettles are also full of iron, vitamin C and calcium too. Too bad they sting or I'd be chomping on one right now.

And that's the end of the game and indeed our look at chatterbox plants. If you answered all the questions correctly, thank you for saving my life: you're now a qualified doctor.* And if you got any of these questions wrong, you're only seven years' training away from being a qualified doctor.**

(*not legally binding)

(**also not legally binding)

BITESIZE NATURE TABLE

Before we move on to our next *Nature Table* group, here are some quick wildlife facts for your brain to absorb.

Did you know...?

Dragonflies and damselflies form a heart shape with their tails when they mate. Scientists are still trying to prove if this is just for their Instagram likes.

The Earth has more than 80,000 species of edible plants – so my question is – why do we keep persevering with kale?

A group of porcupines is called a 'prickle'. But a singular porcupine that stabs you in the hand is just a plain old 'prick'.

Peaches, apricots and strawberries are all members of the rose family. So, no matter what my partner says, spilling a load of jam onto the bed *is* technically very romantic.

HIGH ACHIEVERS

The next A-list *Nature Table* group we're looking at are the High Achievers. And by this I don't mean they do lots of revision for their exams, going on to get well-paid jobs working for banks or tech start-ups. After all, when did you last see a panda using a calculator? Or a crab reading Ha-Joon Chang's *Economics: The User's Guide*? Exactly... it's not a thing. What I mean by High Achievers are members of the animal kingdom who are perfectly adapted to travelling high up in the air and thriving there.

Let's kick off with high achievers that I reckon will come as a surprise to many of you...

Flying Spiders

Yes, I'm afraid you've read that right. I haven't opened this section with a typo. And I'm not pitching an underwhelming follow-up to the Hollywood blockbuster *Snakes on a Plane*. The fact is we have flying spiders. Or to put it another way, many different types of spiders can fly. I'm sorry, there's no way of sugar-coating it. Spiders are hotshot aviators of the animal kingdom! Let me explain…

Spiders have been recorded flying as high up as 4km (2.5 miles) in the air. And when they're taken up into a jet-stream, spiders have even travelled across seas! Surely it can't be long before you go to the cinema and hear the words, 'Shiver me mandibles! It's Long John Spider and his eight wooden legs.'

'But spiders don't have wings!' you cry. You're not wrong. You're asking yourself how spiders can fly, without wings, rocket boosters or access to air miles? I'm chuffed to say that top wildlife biologist Lizzie Daly joined us on the show and explained all…

Spiders fly, via a method known as 'ballooning'

Every spring groups of spiders gather together, buy themselves a hot-air balloon and do a seven-day intensive balloon-training course. *'Ken's Intermediate Ballooning for Spiders'* in Somerset is especially popular among the spider-ballooning community. With Ken's course completed – and their ballooning certificates achieved – spiders can put on their little flying goggles and chocks away!

Of course I'm talking nonsense. Here's what Lizzie Daly really said about spiders 'ballooning'…

In order to fly, spiders climb to as high a point as possible. They stick their abdomens in the air, release some silk and away they go. The fine gossamer silk that a spider fires out forms a triangular parachute. The parachute carries the spider up into the air, like a balloon, even when there's just the slightest breeze. And because spiders are light, once the parachute lifts them they move very FAST.

So, how do we know about this 'ballooning'?

The phenomenon of spiders 'ballooning' has been known since the time of Aristotle. But in 1827, the first precise observations were published by arachnologist John Blackwell, in a paper he wrote for the natural history journal, the 'Transactions of the Linnean Society.'

A few years later, in October 1832, as he travelled round the world on his ship HMS *Beagle*, eminent Victorian naturalist and celebrated beard-operator Charles Darwin reported seeing spiders floating and landing on board ship. Darwin noted the sighting at sea, 100km from Buenos Aires. He believed it was thermals (warm upward air currents) that were enabling spiders to travel these large distances. So, since then, we've always assumed that some form of breeze is required for spiders to fly... UNTIL NOW. Pioneering studies in the last few years have demonstrated that spiders are also able to take off and fly when there is no breeze. And before you ask, it sadly doesn't involve a miniature spider jet pack.

How do spiders fly without a breeze?

Scientists at the University of Bristol believe they've found the answer. Spiders 'balloon' without any wind by harnessing electric and atmospheric fields to help them fly. Specifically, electro-magnetic fields in the atmosphere help provide the spiders with the required initial force to lift them up, enabling take-off and then continued flight. That's right: spiders can take off and fly without need for a breeze. The plot thickens!

What are electro-magnetic fields? How does this actually work?

The team at the University of Bristol have discovered that spiders can essentially surf our Earth atmosphere's electric charges. I appreciate what I'm saying is complicated and hard to picture. So, here's a brief bit of science to help explain, alongside an accompanying illustration (to make the picture easier to picture... you know what I mean).

The Earth's atmosphere (the air) is always positively charged. In contrast, the Earth's ground and plants are always negatively charged. When a spider crawls onto a plant or any high point (like the leaves on a tree) it's effectively positioning itself on top of a lightning rod. As the spider fires its silk parachute, the silk strands are negatively charged (because the spider is stood on the negatively charged tree).

Negative charges repel each other. So, with both the tree and the spider's silk parachute being negatively charged, they repel one another. So, the spider's parachute is repelled, pushed up and the spider takes off. Now, with the

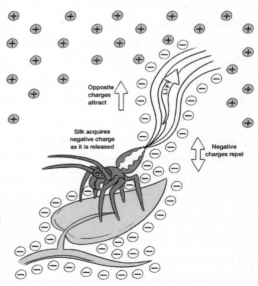

spider airborne, the negative charge of the silk is attracted to the positive charge of the surrounding air (opposite charges attract), which helps give the spider lift and enables it to fly.

Can large spiders also go 'ballooning'? (I'm asking for a friend)

Previously, people assumed that 'spider ballooning' was restricted to either smaller adult spiders or tiny young spiderlings after hatching. The logic being that a bigger spider might be too big and heavy to take off. However, we now know that large adult female velvet spiders (weighing more than 100mg, with a body size of 14mm – that's big by the way!) have been seen ballooning on hot days without wind. These spiders are harnessing electro-magnetic fields via a parachute with a whopping 1m circumference! So, I'm sorry to break it to you: large spiders also fly! Good luck sleeping tonight…

Unsurprisingly, 'ballooning' is dangerous for spiders. Landing from a great height – and at speed – can come at a cost. But with eight legs on their body, if they break one when landing, spiders still at least have seven to work with. I appreciate that last sentence reads a bit heartless Dickensian workhouse, but spiders are good survivors. It's common to see a spider with seven or fewer legs. In fact, when a spider gets its leg trapped, it can self-amputate at a specific joint, dropping the leg to free itself. Spiders are tough!

All this talk of spider flying is seriously impressive and a little bit terrifying. But amongst all this detail, I know there's one question you really want answered. I see it in your eyes. So, let me put it this way… as far as we know, there's no such thing as a spider mile-high club. Spiders still have to mate on land.

AMAZING BONUS SPIDER FLYING FACT:

A clear link has been discovered between spiders ballooning and their ability to survive afloat on water. Water-repellent legs enable spiders to navigate fresh and salt water waves up to 50cm in height. In wind, many species of spider will raise their legs or abdomens to use as sails, propelling themselves across the water's surface. Many species also drop silk to anchor themselves in place while afloat. So yep, I'm sorry to break it to you... spiders can sail. There's literally no escape!

So, now we know the incredible, surprising fact that spiders can fly (and sail), how about we take a cheeky look at some of the other unexpected skills that animals are concealing from us?

Let's play a quick game of the hip new game I'm calling...
True or False?

1.	The plumed basilisk lizard can run on water. True or False?
ANSWER:	**It's true!** When they sense danger, a plumed basilisk can dash across the surface of the water using their hind legs to create pockets of air which keep them afloat.

This lizard is also called the 'What the...? lizard' because when you see it running towards you, you think 'What the??!!!'

2.   **Some birds have developed teeth. True or False?**

ANSWER: **It's false!** Of course birds don't have teeth. Though some birds do have tooth-like ridges in their beaks, birds with actual teeth is just the stuff of a very specific nightmare or new Hollywood blockbuster.

3.   **African hairy frogs can create their own claws out of bone. True or False?**

ANSWER: **It's true!** When threatened, the African hairy frog will break its toe bones causing them to protrude through the skin and use them as makeshift claws to fight off any attackers. Well, that's the last time you start a fight with a frog.

4.   **Some species of jellyfish are immortal. True or False?**

ANSWER: **It's true!** When *Turritopsis dohrnii* jellyfish reach the end of their adult life, they restart their life cycle, transforming back into a polyp. Then Rafiki lifts that polyp up above his head on Pride Rock and they sing 'Circle of Life'. Admittedly 50 per cent of that is made up. The first bit is true. Honest.

5. **Coyotes in the wild have been known to cook their food on hot stones before eating it. True or False?**

ANSWER: **That's utterly false.** I mean where would they find the tongs to flip it over?

6. **A spiny mouse can regrow bits of its own body. True or false?**

ANSWER: **It's true!** The spiny mouse is the only known mammal that has genes that allow it to regenerate. It can regrow skin, cartilage, fur and even sweat glands if they're removed. Truly the only pet that's genuinely for life and not just for Christmas.

And that's the end of this imaginatively titled game of **True or False?** I think it's fair to say we've all learned something, mainly that mankind is doomed.

So, now I've scared you with talk of flying spiders, how about we take a look at another of nature's impressive soaring high achievers…

Cape Vulture

Vultures are spectacular high achievers. And yet they get a bad rap from us. When we think of vultures we often picture big, balding birds scavenging on the ground, feeding on the remains of a dead animal. Our first impression is that they're kind of gross. But, as you're about to discover, there's so much more to vultures than our lazy preconceptions.

The fact is, vultures are brilliant. They just don't have as skilled a PR team as antioxidant fruits like blueberries and goji berries. Vultures are remarkable high achievers, and in more ways than one…

Once again, zoologist Lucy Cooke joined us on the show to speak up for Cape vultures, also known as Cape griffons.

Cape vultures are endemic to southern Africa. They nest in small colonies on cliffs, lay one egg per year and can fly hundreds of kilometres for food. These large endangered birds aren't just impressive in their size; they're inspiring in all sorts of fabulous ways. Here are some quick Cape vulture facts to get us started…

FACT 1: Cape vultures (and in fact all vultures) are BIG BIRDS! Adult Cape vultures commonly grow to 110cm in length. Their large feathers will grow to 70cm long and they have a massive total wingspan of approximately 2.5m. Cape vultures have distinctive bald heads and necks, with long, hooked beaks. Overall, they're creamy white in colour.

FACT 2: Unlike Count Dracula, Count Duckula or indeed Superman, Cape vultures don't actually wear capes. The name 'Cape vulture', comes from the fact that they live around the Cape of southern South Africa.

FACT 3: Cape vultures have an impressive potential lifespan of over 30 years. And whilst we're talking about age, did you know that the longest-living longfin eel – an eel native to New Zealand and Australia – reached the ripe old age of 106?! Imagine how absent-minded it must have become, swimming around the Pacific Ocean thinking, 'I'm sure I left my keys here somewhere…'

USEFUL HOW TO IDENTIFY A VULTURE TIP:

In case you find yourself in Africa wondering if a bird is a vulture or not, here's a practical tip. Real-life vultures don't resemble the Beatles (with moptop hairstyles) or speak with Liverpool accents. If you happen upon one that does, you're likely watching the classic 1967 Disney film, *The Jungle Book*.

High achieving masters of the air

To get a true sense of their brilliance, let's first consider the Cape vulture's humungous wingspan. For context, its 2.5m wingspan is the equivalent height of an adult African forest elephant. It's HUGE! And it's this massive wingspan that makes vultures the kings and queens of the sky. In fact, as Lucy Cooke suggested, the best way to appreciate high achieving vultures is in flight.

But surely, you might ask, when you're a hefty 11-kg Cape vulture, getting off the ground and staying airborne should zap an impossibly huge amount of your energy? It shouldn't be possible.

You're absolutely right, it shouldn't be possible. But Cape vultures are smart birds with a fiendish solution. They wait for the high-up cliff rocks they roost on to warm up. As the day progresses and the sun warms the rocks, so the rocks reflect the sun. This creates upward columns of hot air, known as thermals. The vultures take advantage of these rising columns of warm air and the thermals lift the vultures high into the sky, with the minimum of effort. Once they're airborne they surf the thermals, gliding high up and using minimal energy. Pretty smart!

BONUS VULTURE FACT:

If you're still in any doubt about vultures' 'high-achieving' status, then hear this: the Rüppell's griffon vulture is the highest recorded bird in the world. This particular species has officially reached heights of 11,280m!

For context, the Airbus A380 passenger plane flies at a

> height of up to 13,136m. And for further context, 13,136m is the height of 8,450 Lady Gagas giving each other shoulder lifts. Whatever you think of this book, never say I don't try to paint pointless random images in your mind.

Keeping cool

In the sweltering hot climate they inhabit, vultures have evolved an ingenious way to stop themselves overheating. What they do is wear specially constructed vulture hats, similar to those beer-can hats humans sometimes wear, but filled with ice. No they don't. But that would be fun to see, right? Vultures keep cool using a method called urohidrosis. This is a fancy word for saying that vultures frequently pee and poo on their legs to stay cool (a technique also employed by many humans frequenting music festivals every summer – Boom Tish!).

High-achieving self-defence

Vultures also have an incredibly effective self-defence against potential predators: they'll vomit on a would-be attacker. That's right, vultures can projectile vomit their powerful, rancid gastric acid up to 10m! This is worth considering the next time you pick a fight with a vulture. As I see it, if a vulture wants to play Phil Collins' 1984 power ballad 'Easy Lover' on a pub jukebox, let it go.

As I hope you can see, vultures are badass and brilliant. But if you're still umming and ahhhing, I'm confident the following is their 'mic drop' moment…

Vultures – with their excellent cleaning skills – are our saviours

As I mentioned at the top, we often think of vultures as scavengers and being gross. But if it wasn't for vultures finishing off and cleaning the bones of dead carcasses lying in the heat, we'd have mass pestilence caused by rotting dead animals. So, we may perceive vultures as gruesome scavengers with a foul penchant for eating rotting animals, but vultures doing this actively helps make sure that disease doesn't spread.

So, how can vultures eat rotting diseased animals? Do they need a constant supply of Vulture Rennies to ward off heartburn? The fact is vultures have a powerful natural stomach acid. This enables them to eat and break down almost anything they find. Or to put it another way, vultures are nature's Bear Grylls.

I don't know about you, but all this talk of rotting dead animals is making me hungry. So whilst I make myself a toasted anthrax sandwich, how about we play a quick game?

We know that vultures eat all kinds of horrible things – including animal carcasses – without having to drink eight pints of lager first. But do their digestive systems have a limit? Let's find out in an exciting game of **Come Digest with Me**.

Picture this: you're at home and about to have yourself a perfect evening – the bath is run, candles are lit – and you've got your copy of the best-selling *A Housefly Buzzes in the Key of F* to read (available from all good book shops).

But no! The doorbell rings and it's two vultures demanding a meal! Shock horror! There's no food in the kitchen cupboards. You're a great host though, so you see what you have that they might be able to digest...

Obviously, in the cupboard by your front door, you keep a massive pile of bones – you're known for it.

1. **Do you reckon your vulture guests could digest a massive pile of bones?**

ANSWER: **Yes – vultures can definitely digest bones.** In fact bones make up the majority of the diet of the bearded vulture. I suppose in a way it's just taking the hassle out of making stock.

But wait! The vultures are glaring at you: they're still hungry. So, you look in your fridge. All that's in there is a shovel! I'm not judging.

2.   **Would these two vultures be able to digest a shovel?**

ANSWER: **Yes - vultures can eat shovels!** With a pH between 0 and 1, a vulture's stomach acid is so strong it can dissolve metals. They might need a hand chopping it up into pieces though - those claws are terrible for working an angle grinder.

This is unbelievable! The vultures have digested the bones and shovel, but they're still hungry. So you go into the bathroom and pull out a bottle of anthrax. I won't ask why you've got it.

3.   **But can a vulture digest anthrax?**

ANSWER: **Yes! Vultures can digest anthrax easily.** We don't know if they can digest Metallica or Megadeth though.

As well as anthrax, a vulture's stomach can digest the bubonic plague, rabies, cholera and hepatitis. That's your 5 A Day sorted!

The two vultures have downed the bottle of anthrax and they're still peckish! You desperately open your airing cupboard and spot that freshly shot antelope that Amazon sent instead of the exercise bike you ordered.

4. **Could a vulture eat a freshly shot antelope?**

ANSWER: **Actually, no. If an animal has been shot with a lead bullet, the lead will dissolve and poison the vulture.** It's like the NRA slogan goes, guns don't kill vultures: bullets kill them indirectly and over time and it's very sad.

The vultures were too wise to eat the freshly shot antelope. They're staring at you like you might be next on the menu. You look under the sink and – what a relief – in amongst the bleach and shoe polish kit you nicked from a hotel, there's a sausage roll from a 24-hour garage. What do you think?

5. **Can a vulture eat a 24-hour garage sausage roll?**

ANSWER: **That was a trick question. Not even a hungry vulture would try one of those.** Vultures may be scary looking, but they're not stupid.

And that's the end of our special vulture game. Which is just as well, because I don't think I could have stomached much more. (I'm sorry, I'll get my coat...)

So, now you know a lot more about high-achieving vultures, please be sure to show them a bit more respect from now on. Vultures may not be the most beautiful creatures on the outside, but as their spectacular stomachs demonstrate, it's what's on the inside that counts (in the vulture's case, bones, shovels and bubonic plague). And big up you high-achieving vultures! Thank you for helping to keep our planet free of pestilence.

Zombie-Ant Fungus

Our next 'high achiever' is going to surprise you. It's a fungus. Specifically, we're looking at the zombie-ant fungus. And before you ask, don't panic: zombie fungus can't fly. Its high-achieving status comes from a far weirder place.

The zombie-ant fungus is found predominantly in tropical forest ecosystems, in places like Brazil, Australia and Thailand. It is high achieving, but in an especially brutal way. If you're an insect (or you've watched hit HBO fungus-based drama *The Last Of Us*) you'll know that zombie-ant fungus is properly the stuff of nightmares. Here's why...

Zombie-ant fungus is parasitic. It infects insects and other arthropods with its spores – to devastating effect. So, the next time you pick a fight with a zombie-ant fungus, accusing it of being a 'fun guy', you may want to think twice. (I apologise: that last line was written in spore taste. Clearly there's mushroom for improvement with my writing.)

What makes the parasitic zombie-ant fungus such a high achiever?

Lee Davies – the marvellous fungi curator at Kew Gardens – talked us through the zombie-ant fungus's particulars...

Lee explained that the fungus can completely take over an insect's body in order to reproduce! It can actually manipulate and remote-control an insect to do its bidding. And you thought flying spiders were bad.

How does a rainforest fungus do this incredible dastardly thing?

First of all, the zombie-ant fungus fires millions of its spores into the air (spores are microscopic biological particles that allow fungi to be reproduced, similar to seeds in the plant world). The fungus does this so that they can drift and spread across large landscapes.

A spore from the fungus lands on an insect (usually an ant). This spore then bores into the ant's exoskeleton, infecting the ant and slowly taking control of it. Zombie by name, zombie by nature.

As the infection spreads, the ant is compelled to leave its nest for the tropical forest floor: a warmer more humid area, which is better suited to helping the fungus grow. As the fungus grows in strength it releases more chemicals into the ant, coercing the ant into climbing high up a tree. At this point, the fungus is effectively stealing and remote-operating the legs of the ant! Lovely stuff.

Just when you thought it couldn't get any worse for the ant...

By the time the ant climbs a tree, the high-achieving zombie fungus has penetrated and taken over the ant's jaw muscles. Like a sadistic puppeteer, the fungus now forces the ant's jaws to bite into the tree and remain there.

At this point, the fungus's fruiting bodies grow out of the ant's head and shoot spores down onto the ground below, infecting as many insects as possible (including the infected ant's original nest mates) and the fungus's life cycle continues.

So, there you have it! The impressive but disturbing behaviour of the zombie-ant fungus. I assume you've just let out a harrowing gasp. I have and I've written this. As I see it, this fungus makes the alien in the *Alien* films seem like a kind-natured Labrador in comparison.

WHY does the fungus go to all this trouble to spread its spores?

The zombie-ant fungus has one clear simple goal in life: to reproduce and to spread. The way it does this is via wind dispersal of its spores. Wind dispersal is best done from a tall vantage point, high up a tree. So, as you now know, the zombie-ant fungus is a most effective high achiever!

BONUS FUNGI FACT:

We have clear archaeological evidence that humans have used fungi for food, drinks and medicine for at least the last 6,000 years. What's less well known is that fungi are also used to help make Lego. Plastic Lego bricks are made using itaconic acid, derived from species of the *Aspergillus* fungus. Who knew?! And no – you can't eat it.

Did you know there are over 6 million species of fungi in the world. That means there are over 6 million fungi to give names to. This has led to an enormous list of fungi with names that sound, without wanting to be rude to the fungi, absolutely bonkers.

So, we're now going to play a game called **Is it a Fun-gi?** You have to guess if the following names of a fungus are real or made up…

1: **For our opener, how about barometer earthstar. Real fungi or false fungi?**

ANSWER **That's real!** It resembles a puffball when opened. According to some cultures they have healing properties. This may be why it sounds like something Frank Zappa might have named one of his albums – or children.

2.   **How about bonfire cauliflower? Real or fake?**

ANSWER: **This is also a real one!** It's edible and tasty when young and fresh. Though bonfire cauliflower does sound like something you'd name a vegan dish to make it sound more tempting.

3.   **What about the hairy nuts disco? Real fungi or fake fungi?**

ANSWER: **That's real!** Also known as the *Lanzia echinophila*, it's bright orange and grows on the rotting cases of sweet chestnuts. Yum!

4.   **And finally – what about the fingered candlesnuff? It sounds like a Sarah Waters novel... Real or fake?**

ANSWER: **Happily that's also real.** It's a *Xylaria digitata*, often found growing on dead wood. Its close relatives include the dead man's fingers, which I assume is another kind of mushroom, not just the digits of an overly curious forager.

And that's the end of Is it a Fun-gi? – the game that everyone will soon be talking about; not least because it's the first-ever true or false game with no false answers. Whoops! I think the zombie fungus is taking over my brain…

But before the fungus completely takes control of me, we have time for one more high achiever…

Common Swift

Our final high achiever is another impressive high-flying bird: the common swift. Top naturalist and presenter Nick Baker told us all about these miraculous birds when he was a guest on the show.

Not to be confused with American singer-songwriter Taylor Swift, common avian swifts are found across all our continents, except Antarctica, large deserts and the extreme northern hemisphere. Swifts enjoy temperate regions that are neither too hot nor too cold. Somehow this also includes the UK. They migrate vast distances, wintering in the tropics.

To look at, common swifts have a very striking body shape, with long swept-back crescent-shaped wings and a short, forked tail. Different species of swift can vary in size from 9cm in length (the pygmy swift) to 25cm (the purple needletail swift). Common swifts, on average, are 16cm long (roughly the length of two bars of soap and about two-fifths as high as a bowling ball, since you ask).

Screaming swifts

For many of us in the UK, the distinctive sound of swifts – as they return from wintering in Africa – is the sound of summer.

Swifts have a very specific piercing screaming call. In fact, the collective name for a group of swifts is 'a scream'. And this makes sense, as you'll often hear swifts before looking up and seeing them.

Swifts' call is so particular that many people refer to swifts as having 'screaming parties'. This is where two or more birds are flying fast, calling loudly at rooftop height (they tend to nest in holes near roofs).

These screaming parties mean the swifts are likely breeding nearby. And despite them being referred to as 'screaming parties', scientists still haven't been able to prove if any 'partying' actually takes place; be that dancing, eating cheeseballs or playing the physical skill game *Twister*. I'm sorry, this last sentence clearly says a lot more about me than swifts.

Life on the wing

Predominantly aerial birds, swifts are part of the *Apodidae* family. The word '*Apodidae*' derives from the Greek word *apous* which means 'footless'. This is clearly a reference to the fact that swifts have small, weak legs.

Linked to this – and remarkably – swifts spend most of their life 'on the wing'; which means never landing on the ground. It's this near permanent life on the wing that makes these birds so very special and such high achievers. They do almost everything high up in the air: they drink, they feed, they sleep and often mate whilst flying. Some adult swifts can fly continuously for ten months without landing!

Even though swifts never land on the ground, they can stop. They'll briefly rest on the side of a building and have nests to raise their young (often in the roof space under the eaves of old houses and churches). What's incredible is that swift nests are built by both adults out of any material they can gather whilst they're still flying (remember, swifts don't land on the ground).

Long-haul flights

When juvenile swifts leave the nest (or 'fledge' as it's known) they have about three years of being a screamy teenager: flying all the way from places like the UK to Africa, then around Madagascar before returning back to the UK.

Taking one of the longest migration journeys in the world, swifts will fly 22,531km from the UK to Africa and back. It takes around four weeks for swifts to fly from the UK to their winter home in Africa. The young do this journey three times across three years before they breed (swifts pair up for life). During this three-year period journeying between the UK and Africa, it's highly likely the young won't have touched the ground. It's truly staggering!

BONUS AMAZING SWIFT FACT:

Not only do swifts spend so much of their lives flying, but they're also the fastest recorded bird in level flight. In 2010, a swift was recorded flying at 69.3mph (during a mating flight no less!).

So, at nearly 70mph, the common swift is the fastest bird recorded in level flight. Off the back of this fact, how about a cheeky game of the catchily titled:

'What's Faster? A Swift, or the Following Things I'm About to Read Out?'

1. **First, what's faster, a swift or a peregrine falcon?**

ANSWER: **This is a bit of a trick question, because the answer is both.** The peregrine falcon is quicker during a dive, reaching speeds of over 200mph. But at flying level, the swift is... swifter. Though there's no mention of how fast either of them go when they've lost their footing and fallen out of a tree.

2. **A bat? Faster or slower than a swift? QUICK!**

ANSWER: **Bats are faster than birds!** Research has shown that the Brazilian free-tailed bat can move at over 99mph in level flight. Almost 50 per cent faster than the common swift's record, these bats are speedy!

3. How about a cheetah? Faster than a swift?

ANSWER: **It's neck and neck, as the fastest recorded speed of a cheetah is between 68 and 75mph.** Though in a race situation, who knows if the cheetah would follow the rules... That's not a pun. I just don't trust them.

4. And finally – what's faster – a swift or an East Coast commuter train?

ANSWER: **Not as easy to answer as you might think.** The speed limit on the East Coast line is 120mph, but when you average out the time spent idling in a field outside Stevenage – it evens things out a bit. Overall, I'd give it to the swift.

So as you can see, swifts are properly amazing, punching well above their weight.

It's time for us to move on, but first a virtual round of applause for the incredible and varied high achievers! Feel free to applaud for real, but other people on the train may look at you funny.

BITESIZE NATURE TABLE

Before we check out our next group, here are some amazing bizarre facts about the natural world.

Did you know...?

Barn owls have one ear higher than the other. This is great for pin-pointing exactly where sounds are coming from, but it does mean barn owls look ridiculous in sunglasses.

Contrary to popular belief, dogs don't see in black and white. They have dichromatic vision, seeing things in blue and yellow. Dogs are, however, colour-blind in the red and green spectrum, which explains why they're so rubbish at snooker.

85 per cent of plant life is found in the ocean... Little pointer there if you're ever playing 'hide and seek' with a shrub.

Scientists have discovered that some cockroaches get lonely, suffering ill health when not in a group. So if you ever see a cockroach in your kitchen – for their sake – you'd better hope there are thousands more just behind it.

NOT OUR ENEMY

It's time now for us to look at a group of animals that really taps into what *Nature Table* is all about: showing off animals in a surprising, refreshing and hopefully funny light. Challenging people's preconceptions, whilst – we hope – having some fun.

It's just one of those things in life... there are animals we love to hate. Hate is a strong word. I mean there are animals we have trouble seeing the point of. Sometimes we find an animal scary. Or we think it's revolting. Maybe it's smelly. Maybe it's unlucky enough to be scary, revolting AND smelly.

The point is, there are numerous creatures we give a bad rap to, just because they're not cute and cuddly. It reminds me a bit of being picked on at school because I was too tall and had big curly hair (not great when you're a teenage boy). It still hurts, but what I wouldn't do for those Art Garfunkel goldilocks now! Someone actually asked me the other day if I was Phil Collins' brother. If this book goes well, maybe I'll buy myself a rug. I digress...

We humans are very good at being blinkered about the world around us. We like the simplicity of either liking something or hating it. But nothing is ever this clear-cut, especially in the natural world.

Some of my favourite moments on the shows have been when an expert turns the tables on our prejudices about an animal or plant. This role is often taken up by the Natural History Museum's brilliant fly specialist Dr Erica McAlister. Erica will often say something like, 'Ah ha! You think a wasp is rubbish, but here's why they're brilliant…'

I really love it when the experts make me see an animal or plant in a less 'black and white' way. The truth is everything in life is paradoxical and imperfection is something to be embraced (even if it smells).

So, let's see if we can shake things up and convince you that some animals are 'not our enemy'. Call me reckless, but I've chosen to go all-in with our first potentially unpopular critter…

Mosquitos

BOOM! I'm calling in the big guns and starting with mosquitos… the flies that love to bite and that we love to hate. But before I try to persuade you about the positives of mosquitos, let's get up to speed with some general mosquito facts…

- **The word 'mosquito' derives from the Spanish word for 'little fly'.**
  To be fair, the Spanish are spot on: mosquitos are little flies. Typically mosquitos are 3–6mm long. Or, put

another way, a mosquito is roughly half the size of a garden pea (frozen or fresh, I'm not judging).

- **Mosquitos cannot live in temperatures below 10°C**
  So, if you want to avoid mosquitos and their bites, I can recommend both Antarctica and walk-in freezers as excellent places to go on holiday.

- **Mosquitos have amazing hearing**
  Did you know that some mosquitos can hear sounds as far away as 10m? So think twice before you swear at a mosquito. You'll likely hurt its feelings.

Mosquitos have been on this Earth a very, very long time

Mosquitos date back to the time of the dinosaurs, evolving around 200 million years ago. Some prehistoric mosquitos have been preserved in amber. Those of you who know the film *Jurassic Park* will remember it was thanks to an ancient mosquito encased in amber that actors – pretending to be scientists – were able to extract what the film referred to as 'dino blood'.

On the subject of *Jurassic Park*, here are a couple of handy 'dino facts' that came to light, courtesy of the film:

FACT 1: When a 9-tonne *T-rex* walks, the reverberations are powerful enough to shake a small plastic cup of water sitting on the dashboard of a jeep. FACT.

FACT 2: *Jurassic Park* taught us there were two distinct prehistoric dinosaur types in existence: a) CGI dinosaurs and b) animatronic puppet dinosaurs. FACT

But enough dino-chat. Let's get back to mosquitos and focus on why they're superb...

I know what you're thinking: 'Why should I befriend a mosquito? All they do is bite us and make us itch. Mosquitos suck! [our blood and metaphorically].'

I used to think the same as you, as I doused myself in mosquito repellent. I couldn't see any positive to these small irritating bitey rascals. But then Dr Erica McAlister came on the show and opened everybody's eyes to the total magnificence of mosquitos... Hurray!

Dispelling a common mosquito myth

First off, Erica pointed out that mosquitos are often referred to as 'the deadliest insect on the planet'. But this claim is false: no single mosquito has ever killed a human. It would take between 200,000 and 2 million mosquitos – in one giant feeding banquet – to kill one human from blood loss. This is clearly an impractical way to kill someone, but a potential plot-twist in a Richard Osman penned murder mystery. The truth is you're more likely to die from forgetting how to breathe than by a mosquito's mandibles (jaws to you and me).

Erica then said something that came as a big surprise. A surprise that properly blew my mind and made me re-evaluate my view of mosquitos. Erica explained that by learning HOW mosquitos bite us, we could deliver a major benefit to the human race...

Smart needles inspired by mosquitos.

Adult female mosquitos have what's called a 'proboscis' (a long tube-like mouth). This proboscis enables female mosquitos to pierce an animal's skin and feed on their blood. Blood is a great source of protein and iron (as Count Dracula once told me over lunch), which helps female mosquitos produce their eggs.

BONUS MOSQUITO BITING FACT:

Only female mosquitos bite animals for blood. Male mosquitos are vegetarian (which explains why male and female mosquitos on a first date will often compromise by sharing a plate of Quorn Scotch Eggs).

When a mosquito bites you, you don't feel the bite or the itch. The itching only begins AFTER the bite, once the mosquito has flown away. The itch and ensuing rash are an aftershock of the mosquito bite. The reason we don't clock the bite as it happens is because female mosquitos – via their tube-like proboscis mouth – can first penetrate our skin and then move their mouth parts under our skin without causing us any pain.

How do they do this?

The mosquito's proboscis injects us first with the female's saliva. This saliva numbs our skin (reducing pain, but leaving us with the rash and itch afterwards). In addition, the proboscis is designed to be softer near the tip. This minimises the force required to pierce the skin, which again causes us less pain, meaning we don't feel anything and remain blissfully unaware.

Scientists are getting close to successfully developing painless smart needles – inspired by the mosquito's mouth parts – which means we could have medical syringes that don't hurt us. How cool is that? No one likes needles, so if we can remove the pain and fear of having a jab, more people around the world will come forward to be immunised and more lives will be saved. Rather than being our enemies, there's actually a lot we're learning from these perfectly designed mosquitos. So, next time you want to rubbish a mosquito to its face, maybe reconsider.

This is amazing life-changing science, but I do appreciate that most of you reading this won't think it compensates for the aggro of an itchy bite. Let me give you some more benefits to being pals with mosquitos...

Mosquito saliva could help us fight blood clots

A team at the University of Sydney has discovered that the proteins in a mosquito's saliva have anti-clotting properties. When a mosquito bites and its saliva passes into an animal, the saliva helps give the mosquito better access to the blood meal.

By mimicking the anti-clotting properties of a mosquito's saliva, scientists are developing new drugs to treat conditions like deep vein thrombosis and strokes. So, if we change our viewpoint and positively embrace mosquitos (not like that – you'd squish them) they'll help us to tackle the fatal impact of blood clots on humans. Seriously, how about a round of applause for mosquitos and their anti-clotting saliva!! Anyone??!

Important pollinators

As Erica further explained, another reason we should be wining and dining mosquitos is because they're expert pollinators. Specifically, mosquitos enable plants to fertilise and produce new plants. This directly helps us humans, by giving us a whole bunch of fruit and veg to eat. Thanks, mosquitos!

Some of you are maybe starting to see the positives of mosquitos. But I reckon many of you are still thinking, 'Computer says no.' To those naysayers, let me finish with a bit of practical science that might help you share this Earth with mosquitos in a more positive fashion…

Sniffing out danger

In 2018, researchers at the University of Washington wrote a paper suggesting mosquitos can learn to link a particular smell with danger and avoid it next time.

So, let's imagine you try to swat a mosquito. Most of the time you'll miss (because mosquitos are too quick). But the mosquito will associate YOUR smell – at the precise moment you swatted – with danger and steer clear of you in future. It turns out mosquitos remember smells, so the instant it got a fright, it now knows to avoid you and your smell.

In this 2018 study, mosquitos clearly linked the human smell with danger. But it was apparently less successful with mosquitos and the smell of chicken. What I want to know is how the researchers trained chickens to use fly swats? Moving on...

These findings could have important implications for future mosquito control. And in the meantime, if you're a terrible shot and 'swat and miss' a bunch of times, mosquitos should remember your smell and leave you alone. Scared mosquitos = no biting (in theory!).

So, that's our look at clever mosquitos. I appreciate it's a tall order convincing people that mosquitos aren't our enemy. But I hope by knowing more about them, by knowing that they could help us, you can now see some positives. In some respects, mosquitos could actually become our saviours. So I reckon a bit more respect for them wouldn't go amiss. Please and thank you.

Let's leave mosquitos to do their thing and move on to our next animal that gets a raw deal from us human peoples...

SHARKS

Let me introduce you to a well-known, renowned star of the Hollywood screen. A certain pointy-finned fish... the humble shark.

Before you put your hand up and scream, 'Of course I have a problem with sharks; they're brutal relentless killing machines, you idiot!', please consider this. Right now, shark numbers around the world are diminishing. In fact, some are close to extinction. On *Nature Table*, we've had many experts speak in defence of sharks.

The truth is, sharks are majorly misunderstood and misrepresented by us. We need to stop basing our view of these remarkable fish on the entertaining but far-fetched exploits of a single mechanical rubber shark from the 1970s and 80s. I am of course referring to 'Bruce': the often-malfunctioning radio-controlled co-star of four *Jaws* films.

I'm guilty of being a massive *Jaws* fan. I first saw the film when I was five years old (what was my best friend's older brother thinking). I spent the next 12 months nervously sitting on the loo, thinking that Jaws was going to bite my bum. I was also convinced that Jaws would join me in the bath, via the plughole. I was an impressionable five-year-old with a vivid imagination. The film *Jaws* left me scared of sharks.

Thankfully I now realise that these films – and other films like *The Meg* – paint a ludicrous, one-dimensional image of sharks as relentless killers. Some scientists have actually referred to it as 'The Jaws Effect' – our misguided belief that sharks are intentionally seeking out, hunting and killing humans.

As you're going to find out, sharks aren't our enemy. They're not interested in us as a meal. I'm sorry to break this to you, but we're not their type! We're going to dispel some classic shark clichés by looking at two very different types of amazing shark in this section.

I wonder who our first shark is going to be. Oh, hang on, I can hear some orchestral music starting to fade up. It sounds like: Da-dunnnnn… Da-dunnnnn…. Da-dunnnn….. Dun… Dun… Dun… Dun… Dun… Dun… Dun… Dun… Dun Dunnn…

Great White Shark

How did you guess? It's the great white shark. The shark that scares us more than any other but is also one of the most misunderstood and unfairly maligned creatures on Earth. Classified as 'vulnerable' due to its rapidly shrinking numbers, great whites are amazing impressive fish. But before we explore why great white sharks are so great, let me share some inspiring opening facts with you…

FACT 1: Male great white sharks are generally 3.5–4m long, while females are 4.5–5m. The largest recorded great white shark was a female measuring 5.8m long. Or the equivalent height of 76 stacked Rubik's Cubes.

FACT 2: Great white sharks weigh approximately 2,000kg. This is roughly the same weight as a large saloon car, with sat nav and electric windows. And before you ask, Great whites don't come with sat nav or electric windows as standard. However, air-con (via the great white's gills) is found on all models.

FACT 3: Great whites can live to an impressive 70 years or more. Males take 26 years to reach sexual maturity and females 33 years. That's a lot of time thinking about the birds and the bees. Or in the case of great whites, the clams and the winkles.

FACT 4: Great white sharks have approximately 300 5-cm long teeth. However, across a great white's lifetime, they can get through 20,000 teeth. This is because they have a never-ending supply of new teeth. Whenever a great white breaks a tooth or it falls out, a new row of teeth rolls forward; a bit like crisp packets moving forward in a vending machine. No need to fork out on dentist bills then.

FACT 5: Great whites can swim to incredible depths – 1,200m – and have a top speed of 25mph. This swim speed is ten times faster than an average human swimmer and is incredible for such a large heavy fish. But let's face it, at 25mph, you know there'll be a long tailback of frustrated swordfish pulling caravans on their way to Mallorca.

Great white misunderstood sharks

These eye-catching stats and facts I've just shared all add up to make great white sharks an *apex predator*. This is a name we give to animals that have no natural predators. Regularly referring to great whites as apex predators has created a sense that great whites are top dogs (well, top fish) of the ocean. We assume that they're untouchable. That no other creature would ever mess with one. But we are wrong…

Great whites, orcas and dolphins

Question: What animal could possibly hunt an apex predator like a great white shark?

Answer: It turns out there's another apex predator of the sea. One that's a bit more apex than great whites. Orcas (killer whales) hunt great white sharks.

Between May and July 2017, it was reported that four great white sharks washed up on the beaches of South Africa. They were all missing their livers. The deaths were proven to be caused by orcas, who likely ate the sharks' livers for their high fat and nutrients. So, even when you're a great white shark, there's always a bigger fish (well, similarly-sized mammal, but you know what I mean). Shock horror: great white sharks are vulnerable.

But it's not just orcas that can challenge great whites and win. Dolphins will get in on the action too. Like their cousins, the orcas, pods of dolphins will work together to harass and sometimes attack great white sharks.

Question: So how is it that orcas and dolphins can successfully challenge great whites?

Answer: Orcas and dolphins are able to harass and beat great white sharks thanks to their body design…

Orcas and dolphins have flexible skeletons. In contrast, sharks are cartilage-filled. This means orcas and dolphins can manoeuvre their bodies more swiftly.

Orcas and dolphins have horizontal tails, because they've evolved from four-legged mammals with limbs underneath their bodies. Meanwhile great whites, which are fish, have vertical tails.

Orcas and dolphins, with their backbones that naturally bend up and down, can move up or down with much more agility than sharks with their vertical plane tails. This means that orcas and dolphins are far more nimble than great whites. This gives them the advantage over the shark in a fight.

Orca and dolphin snouts are made of very tough thick bone. They're nature's battering rams. Orcas and dolphins are known to position themselves several yards under a great white shark and burst upwards, jabbing their snout into the soft underbelly of the shark and causing serious internal injuries.

All these different factors in the body design of orcas and dolphins combine to make them more than a match for great white sharks. It's remarkable, and completely dispels the myth of great whites being untouchable. 'Smiley' mammals like dolphins and orcas can take on great whites and win.

Great white clichés

It was a real pleasure when multi-award-winning wildlife cameraman Doug Allan joined us on the show, speaking in support of great white sharks. Doug has spent many hours in the water with great whites and was able to shed light on what really makes them tick.

For starters, when you see a great white, be that a photo or footage, they always look scary. Most of the time it's that iconic image: they have their mouths wide open, showing us their 300 or so pointy teeth. They look menacing. It looks like they're ready to bite at any moment. Who wouldn't be scared?

But great whites have no choice but to show off their pearly whites! The truth is they have to keep their mouths wide open most of the time because they need a huge amount of oxygen to survive.

You see, great whites don't have lungs. Instead they take water in through their mouth – using muscles in their cheeks – to absorb the water's oxygen and then push the excess water out through their gills. So, great white sharks aren't showing us their serrated teeth to terrify us; their gobs are open so they can breathe!

Great whites aren't interested in eating us

Doug explained that great white sharks are very specific and particular when it comes to food. It turns out that we humans – with all our bones – aren't a great white's menu preference.

On the rare occasion that a great white attacks a human, it's usually a mistake. For a great white looking up from the deep, a swimmer or surfer on the surface of the water can resemble a seal (fatty seals are a great white's preferred meal). The shark sees a silhouette on the surface and mistakenly attacks. It's a mistake in the same way that I tell my partner I've mistaken a bag of Fruit Pastilles for an apple. I'm sorry, I'm being facetious. Great whites aren't interested in eating us. Their relationship with humans is more like my relationship with stinky mouldy blue cheese – gross! No, thank you!

When you read or hear about great whites attacking people, it's always the same story. The shark takes one bite and as soon as it realises the human isn't a seal, they back off. Unlike the malfunctioning relentless rubber shark in *Jaws,* real great whites aren't out to attack and kill us for food.

In fact, statistically, cows are deadlier than great whites. Maybe you saw the viral meme from a few years back, 'Every year sharks kill 10 people. Every year, 100 people die from being stepped on by cows.'

The fact-checking publication, *Snopes*, investigated the above claim in 2023. The meme originally dated back to 2013. *Snopes* found that only five shark attacks resulted in deaths in 2022.

Whilst in 2021, cattle-ranching-related fatal injuries in just the USA amounted to 96. As a result Snopes concluded: 'Based on the available data from just the US and a few other countries, on average more people are killed annually by cows than sharks.'

★ **SUPER BONUS GREAT WHITE SHARK FACT:**

Did you know that great whites communicate through body language? Arching their bodies, opening their jaws and nodding their heads are all signals that great whites use to talk to one another.

It's also been recorded that when two great whites are after the same prey, they'll put on a slapping display to try to deter the other.

So, next time you see a great white arch its body, open its jaws and nod its head at you, don't panic. It may well be trying to point out that you still have a bit of mayonnaise on your lip.

To summarise, as Doug Allan and science tells us, great white sharks aren't mindless fierce fish, desperate to hunt and eat us. Great whites aren't our enemy.

But if you're still doing your unconvinced face, here are some final positive reasons for giving great white sharks a break...

- **Great whites help us fight climate change...**
  Carbon is a by-product of life and contributes to climate change. All animals contain carbon, and by eating dead

matter that collects on the sea floor great whites help to recycle and remove carbon from the bottom of the ocean. Without great whites this carbon would rise to the surface. It's been estimated that sharks remove up to half the manufactured carbon in the atmosphere. So, without the help of sharks it would be game over for the Earth much sooner.

- **Great whites help fight climate change a second way**
  In the ocean, meadows of seagrass and kelp capture carbon from the atmosphere 35 times faster than tropical rainforests. Great white sharks, wearing their apex predator hats, are vital because they prevent other species – such as sea turtles – from overgrazing on the seagrass and kelp. This means the carbon-capturing plant life flourishes, thus keeping CO_2 levels down.

So, great white sharks are helping us fight climate change in two different ways. A round of applause please, for these marvellous planet-saving fish!

- **Great white sharks may have cures for diseases**
  Shark tissue appears to have anti-coagulant and anti-bacterial properties. Researchers believe this may explain why sharks don't get ill as frequently as other animals. Off the back of this, a group of scientists at the University of Florida have been studying great white DNA and discovered 'mutations' in it.

Specifically, great whites have evolved DNA that can repair itself. This ability to stabilise their genomes protects great whites from illnesses like cancer. In contrast, we humans have unstable genes, which makes us prone to disease. Shark DNA is 1.5 times bigger than human DNA, which means there are things coded into shark DNA that we don't have.

If we can discover how great whites repair their DNA, this could be a massive game-changer for human health. So, the animal that we're scared of could well be the key to our survival. Funny old world, isn't it…

So, that's the magnificent great white shark. Despite what Hollywood wants us to think, I hope you now see that great whites aren't out to get us. If anything, the opposite is true: great white numbers are decreasing due to the many years of hunting by us for their fins, for their meat and their teeth.

The sea is the great white's home. When we go into the sea – whether that's in a boat or swimming – we need to be respectful. The sea is their right of way, not ours. And this is coming from a man who spent 12 months of his childhood terrified that a shark would bite his bottom on the loo. If even I can now see how tremendous and misunderstood great whites are, then I hope you can too. As entertaining as films like *Jaws* are, we must realise they're nothing more than popcorn fiction. Before it really is too late for the jaw-droppingly wondrous great white sharks.

Now, many animals get a bad press from us humans. But as we've seen, sharks really do get more than their fair share. So, I want us to say hello to a very different, but equally illuminating, shark. A shark that really shows off these fantastic fish in a very different empathetic light. Apologies in advance, this shark's name sounds like something you might find on a Heston Blumenthal menu. But don't let that put you off. Please put your hands and fins together for the very marvellous and surprisingly sociable...

Lemon Shark

Contrary to what you may think, lemon sharks aren't so-called because they're citrus fresh; truth be told, they smell pretty fishy. Lemon sharks get their name because of their distinctive yellow colouring. Their body colour helps them camouflage when swimming over bright, shallow sandy seafloors.

Growing up to 3.4m in length, lemon sharks live in shallow subtropical mangroves, from the Gulf of Mexico to the Ivory Coast. Alongside great whites, lemon sharks are classified as a vulnerable species by the International Union for the Conservation of Nature. And as you're about to find out, lemon sharks have a surprising characteristic, helping to dispel the myth of sharks being terrifying monsters...

Sociable sharks

What makes lemon sharks so striking – aside from their racy body colour – is their propensity for social behaviour. In contrast with many other sharks, lemon sharks choose to live in large groups. They thrive on social interaction. Indeed, the shallow mangrove areas where these sharks live are often referred to as 'nursery sites'. Lemon sharks commonly remain in the same area they were born, or regularly return to breed. Home is where the heart is!

Ace zoologist and conservationist Megan McCubbin appeared on the show to speak up for lemon sharks. Megan has researched lemon sharks up-close at Bimini Bay in the Bahamas. She and the team's research focused on the social behaviour of these creatures. Specifically, they wanted to learn more about lemon sharks' personalities. What Megan and the research team discovered was astounding!

Lemon shark personality: Friendly? Nervous? Sarcastic?

So, what kinds of personality do lemon sharks have? And how on Earth do you go about doing a personality test on a shark?!

For us humans, figuring out our personality type is pretty straightforward. We can go online and fill out a 'personality test', answering a number of questions to help build up a personality profile. But it's not so simple with lemon sharks. Getting a shark to go online and answer a personality test is nigh on impossible. For starters, lemon sharks have real trouble turning on a router or holding a pencil. To properly get to the bottom of what makes a shark's brain tick, a different approach is required.

What Megan and the team of researchers did was put the lemon sharks into large pens for a week, before releasing them. Whilst in these pens, novel objects were put into the water and the team checked how the sharks reacted. Specifically, they were looking at which sharks approached the unusual items and which stayed away. And from there they could start building a portrait of the sharks' personalities.

Lemon sharks have big personalities!

The research at Bimini Bay proved that lemon sharks have clearly defined and different personalities! In terms of social behaviour, they found that lemon sharks with similar personalities hang out in groups. Like-minded lemon sharks stay together.

What Megan and the team noted was that the confident sharks – who were interested in the novel objects – hung out in one group. And then the more nervous, reticent sharks – who stayed back and didn't approach the unusual items – also formed a group. It's a bit like the group cliques you get at school: over there are the confident sporty sharks, then there's the nervous academic sharks. And next to them are the angsty emo sharks. Just like children in a playground, like-minded sharks form groups and hang out!

This amazing research shows off sharks in a fresh new light. As I mentioned earlier, we tend to think of sharks as being fearless: solitary apex predators who are scared of nothing. But we now know, just like you and me, sharks have personalities. Some sharks are bold and inquisitive. Some sharks are shy and stand-offish. So here's to meeting up with the shy academic chess-playing sharks the next time we swim in the sea!

BONUS LEMON SHARK FACT:

Lemon sharks are nocturnal feeders, able to sense their prey (other fish) in the dark. They can do this thanks to electroreceptors in their head. These electroreceptors detect electrical pulses sent out by a potential prey, enabling the shark to pinpoint exactly where the prey is. Unfortunately the same electroreceptors aren't able yet to locate pieces of Lego on the floor or lost car keys.

All this talk of lemon sharks has given me an idea for a game...

The whimsically named lemon shark isn't the only aquatic creature named after a fruit or other foodstuff – the sea is full of species who got their names because the scientist who discovered them was feeling a bit peckish at the time. Let's find out more with a round of the potentially Bafta-winning game... **Fish Food!**

I'm going to give you a marine animal that's named after another foodstuff and you're going to tell me if it's real or something I've cooked up.

1.   **Let's start with the fried egg jellyfish – is this real or just the least popular Haribo Tangfastic?**

ANSWER: **It's REAL.** It may shock you to know the fried egg jellyfish got its name because it looks almost exactly like a fried egg. In fact, the best way to tell the two apart is that a fried egg is unlikely to be swimming in the Mediterranean.

2. **How about the orange-peel doris – is this a real sea creature? Or an old lady who sits at the front of the bus ostentatiously peeling citrus fruit?**

ANSWER: **It's REAL!** The orange-peel doris is a mollusc that turns bright orange to warn predators it's toxic, and has an awful taste. A bit like those kids who drank too much Sunny D.

3. **How about the coconut clam – is this a shellfish mollusc so-named because of its hardened, hairy, coconut-like shell?**

ANSWER: **It's FALSE!** There is no such thing as a coconut clam. But we do have coconut crabs – a crab that can grow up to 90cm wide and eats birds. Now you know it exists... don't go having nightmares!

4.   **And finally – how about the garlic
      bread sea cucumber – is it real or just
      a side dish that comes with its own
      side salad?**

ANSWER: **It's REAL!** The garlic bread sea
          cucumber is around 20–40cm long and
          has tiny tube feet all over its body –
          which makes me wonder what kind of
          awful Italian restaurants the scientist
          who named it had been eating at.

And the sound of that gong you can't read means the end of this
rather silly but factually accurate game. Please feel free to wow
your friends and/or enemies with your newfound expertise for
animals with food-based names. You're very welcome!

So now I've hopefully made you think twice about mosquitos
and sharks, I'm going to up the ante and make you think thrice,
with another unloved animal. An animal that deserves a more
positive press than it gets.

It's time for me to put everything on red and see if I can sway
you regarding one of our planet's least appealing creatures. Wish
me luck, as I ask you to befriend…

Maggots

KAPOW! Yes, we're talking about maggots! By the time I've finished discussing maggots, I guarantee they'll be everyone's best friend![2]

But first, here's a question to open with:

What is a maggot?

A maggot is technically the larval stage of a fly; the in-between stage of a fly's egg and its pupa. The average maggot's lifespan is eight to ten days. Looking sort of like a very small worm, maggots are only 3–10mm in length and don't have arms or legs. But boy can they sing! And when I say sing, I mean wriggle.

Why do we give maggots such a bad rap?

On a visual level, maggots look slimy and grubby. They're not exactly appealing to the eye. Which, to be fair, isn't the maggots' fault. What are maggots supposed to do, have plastic surgery? We're in the middle of a cost-of-living crisis and maggots don't have unlimited funds for plastic surgery. Before we know it, there could be a massive rise in puffy-faced maggots robbing banks to feed their plastic surgery addictions. No thank you. Not on my watch!

The other issue we have with maggots is linked to their dietary choices: they feed on decaying animals and faeces. As a result, maggots can unknowingly contaminate food that's later consumed by people, leading to infection or disease. In the maggots' defence, the crucial word here is 'unknowingly'. Maggots aren't trying to

---

2 This is not guaranteed.

harm us; it's just that their way of life can cross paths with ours in a negative way. It's not their fault!

I appreciate my saying it's not their fault isn't going to win anyone over. You all still think maggots are awful and you can't see yourself ever becoming friends with one. Perhaps you'd go fishing with one, but we both know how that's going to end...

This is a tough challenge, convincing you of the positives of maggots. Thankfully, I have someone to help me. The genius that is Dr Erica McAlister came on the show to make the case for maggots.

What follows are some staggering positive maggot facts, courtesy of Erica. I'm confident these will have you at least thinking twice about my friend: the armless, legless, challenged-in-the-looks-department maggot...

Maggots solve crimes!

BOOM! That's right, maggots are crime busters.

As we all know from watching our favourite TV detective shows, establishing the time of death is crucial when investigating a murder.

It takes just a few minutes after a death for flies to arrive and start laying eggs. By studying the size and age of maggots on a body, the police can accurately determine the amount of time that's passed since a person died. This form of deduction is so effective that there have been court cases where maggot evidence has been used to successfully prosecute in a murder!

So before you continue dissing maggots, remember: maggots have helped to successfully put human murderers behind bars. Thank you, maggots.

Incredibly, as Erica explained, maggots have been helping murder investigations for the last 800 years. In 1247, in medieval China, the Chinese lawyer Sung Ts'u wrote about a murder that took place near a rice field. The people investigating believed that one worker had killed another worker, using a sickle (a sickle is a tool commonly used for harvesting rice). But since so many workers used sickles, how do you prove who the murderer was?

The local law officer called all the rice field workers together, with their sickles. One of the sickles soon attracted lots of flies and maggots, yet all the sickles looked clean. Even though the sickle the insects were drawn to had been wiped, the flies and maggots could still smell the blood residue and miniscule human tissue left on the metal murder weapon. As a result, the murderer confessed to the crime. Big up the detective skills of flies and DCI Mike Maggot!

EXPERT WITNESS

Maggots save lives!

Not only do maggots help solve murder cases, but they also save human lives. How brilliant is that? Still see them as the enemy?

For a long time (dating back at least to the 1500s) maggots have been used to clean wounds: helping patients with gangrene or ulcerating wounds caused by type 2 diabetes. How it works is the maggots feed on a wound's dead and infected skin tissue, which means the healthy tissue can grow and the wound closes.

Maggots are good enough to leave the healthy flesh alone. That's right: maggots help us heal.

At the same time, maggots can also help us fight an infection. They do this by releasing enzymes that kill bacteria, which stimulates our bodies to heal. The use of maggots in this way is available on the NHS, and is known as larval debridement therapy (LDT), also known as 'maggot therapy'.

And as if maggots saving lives isn't enough to convince you, here's a final pro-maggot fact (or PMF) to sway you...

Maggots are geniuses at decomposing organic matter

By crumbling down organic matter, maggots create rich, nutrient-laden compost, which helps our gardens grow. Recent research has shown that the larvae (maggots) of black soldier flies chomp through organic food and animal waste so quickly that bacteria doesn't have the time to thrive. This cuts down the odours created by the bacteria. As a result, your garden compost won't stink so bad. These wondrous maggots get their meal and we get compost that doesn't stink: it's win-win! Maggots are the blimmin' marvels!

So, that's the case for maggots, M'lud. I hope you're on board with these bona fide marvels. I'm not suggesting you take a maggot on holiday, or buy one an air fryer, but I hope I've convinced you that there's more that's positive to maggots than first meets the eye.

Before we move to our next group, I'd like to add that the same goes for all the animals we've looked at in this section. Be it mosquitos, sharks or maggots: none of these creatures are baddies. Once you know the full picture, you can't help but look at the animal in a more eyes-wide-open way; one that goes beyond just their looks. I do hope that the next time you lay eyes on an animal you're not a fan of, you'll read up on them and give them a second chance. I really enjoy having my animal prejudices challenged and squashed.

BITESIZE NATURE TABLE

Before we deep-dive our next splendid group, here are some more snackable facts to impress your friends, family and business rivals...

Did you know...?

There's a type of ant – nicknamed the Manhattant – that only lives in a small area of New York... Well, you can't blame an ant for wanting to live in a Big Apple.

All orchid flowers are symmetrical. So, if you cut them right down the middle... you'll get shouted at by florists and charged for damages.

A wild turkey's head changes colour depending on its mood. I imagine its least favourite mood is 'festive'.

An apple a day won't actually keep the doctor away. But a well-aimed coconut can keep one out of action for weeks.

DOING IT MY WAY

I'd like to start our look at this new group with a short personal observation. When we make *Nature Table* and hear from leading natural history experts, I love finding out that 'facts' about animals that we assume must be correct – because TV or books have told us they are – are actually clichés and can be debunked.

I think a great example of this can be seen in gender roles. Gender roles in the animal kingdom are way more fluid and interesting than we're often led to believe. In the past, the media has sometimes sold us a version of gender roles in animals that feels like the set-up to a family sitcom from the 1970s. Let me explain…

When you see a pride of lions on a TV documentary, the traditional story we've been told is that male lions go out and hunt – effectively the male goes out to work every day to hunt a crust for the family – whilst the female lions are the home-makers, looking after the children. And the lion cubs are the pesky young kids who keep biting each other and skipping school.

But in reality, it's female lions who go out and hunt most of the prey, not males. It's actually the females who bring back the lion's share for their families, whilst the males stay at home and protect the pride. This explains why male lions in the wild are often seen wearing 'Stay at home Dad' baseball caps.

So with this next collection of animals, a group I've named Doing It My Way, I want to show you just how vast, varied and surprising the animal kingdom can be, and that the animal kingdom isn't a 'one size fits all' place. And when it comes to challenging gender roles, animals really are leading the way.

Let's start this party with a large bird that has pioneered doing life its own way...

Laysan Albatross

Living in the Northwestern Hawaiian Islands, Laysan albatrosses are one of Earth's largest seabirds. Their average body length is a whopping 81cm. With their white heads, blackish-grey upper wings and a distinctive black smudge around the eye, Laysan albatrosses can live upwards of 50 years. In fact, as of 2023, the oldest recorded bird in the world is a female Laysan albatross called Wisdom. At the time of writing this, records show that Wisdom is at least 72 years old! Good on you, Granny Wisdom!

BONUS SHOWBIZ ALBATROSS FACT:

On 11 January 1970, one career-minded albatross turned up on classic BBC TV comedy *Monty Python's Flying Circus*, stealing the show in the celebrated 'Albatross' sketch from Series 1, episode 13. Have a watch online if you don't believe me.

Albatrosses have the largest wingspan of any flying bird

Albatrosses have a record-breaking wingspan of up to 370cm. The Laysan albatross, our focus here, has an impressive average wingspan of 203cm!

Thanks to their massive wings, albatrosses can fly huge distances – approximately 800km per day – as they hunt for their favourite food: squid. And if flying 800km per day doesn't impress you (it's roughly the distance between Bournemouth and Dundee), how about the fact that albatrosses can fly these vast distances with just an occasional flap of their wings?!

How is this possible?

How does such a large bird fly such vast distances with just a few flaps of its wings, and using only a small amount of energy? The answer is evolution, which has made the albatross an absolute genius when it comes to flight. And the secret to this genius can be found in the albatross's bill.

It's all in the nose!

An albatross's bill (or nose) is large, strong and hooked at the end. Running along both sides of the bill are two tubes. These tubes enable albatrosses to measure their exact airspeed whilst in flight. We humans have copied this: all modern aircraft have something similar, known as the 'pitot tube'. By having these tubes along their bills, albatrosses can measure their airspeed accurately and perform what's known as 'dynamic soaring'. Dynamic soaring enables an albatross to fly 800km with just a few flaps of its giant wings. But what is dynamic soaring, I hear you ask? It's complicated, so please bear with me. I'll try to make it as clear as possible... Albatrosses fly vast distances, with minimal effort, by exploiting the differences in wind speeds of two adjacent regions of air, close to the ocean surface. Put simply, albatrosses fly by gliding over the sea. They glide by gently diving down and then gently climbing up in a repeated continuous motion, harvesting energy from the steady flow of wind over the sea. This is what we call dynamic soaring.

Albatrosses' mastery of dynamic soaring means they don't have to flap their wings much and can travel huge distances without getting tired. They are the only species of bird that has truly mastered this low-energy mode of gliding; a clear example of these birds 'doing it their way'. In fact, this mode of flight is so impressive in its energy saving that scientists are studying the albatross's mastery of dynamic soaring to see if they can replicate it for drone technology.

And although this skill stems from their bill, let me clarify that 'dynamic soaring' isn't the same as 'dynamic snoring', which is something I'm frequently accused of. The less we talk about that the better.

As incredible as an albatross's schnoz is at helping it fly long distances, I want to now share a fact that makes Laysan albatrosses bona fide members of the Doing It My Way club. Scientists have discovered a colony of Laysan albatrosses in Hawaii where 30 per cent of the birds are in long-term female/female relationships. Genius zoologist Lucy Cooke came on the show to share more on this incredible discovery...

Why do female Laysan albatross form female/female partnerships?

The first thing to say is that the female Laysan albatrosses at Ka'ena Point Oahu, Hawaii, do mate with males. However, there's a shortage of males at this site (the reason being that the colony at Ka'ena Point is new and male albatrosses tend to stay at the site they were born, whereas females will move on and start new colonies).

So with a lack of males at the new colony site, the female Laysan albatrosses have been monitored 'borrowing' another female's partner and having a sly bit of 'albatross hanky-panky'. The sexually sly female then pairs up with another female to raise the chick.

The reason these single females pair up after copulation is because it takes two albatrosses to not just tango but also to feed, protect and raise a single chick. As the chick grows, one of the adult females protects the chick from predators whilst the other female travels huge distances to hunt for squid and bring it back to the nest.

From the egg first being laid to the chick fledging (becoming capable of flight) albatrosses can spend between six months and a year raising a chick. As you can see, a lot of effort goes into supporting a single albatross chick.

Let's stay together

As I mentioned, female Laysan albatrosses breed with males. But we now have proof that females enter into long-term relationships with other females, even after a chick has been raised. That's right, female albatrosses actively preen one another and do all the romantic relationship stuff, like candle-lit clifftop squid dinners and forgetting their anniversary.

There's one female Laysan albatross couple that has been together for a staggering 17 years. At the time of writing, this couple have raised eight chicks and are grandparents to two. When asked what the secret to a long relationship is they replied, 'Listening is important. And it helps that we both like squid.'

BONUS ALBATROSS FACT:

Albatrosses do elaborate mating dances, with two albatrosses putting on a synchronised performance. The dance involves various seductive moves including preening, calling and bill clacking.

During this mating ritual, the noises albatrosses make have been variously described as: mooing, moaning, whining, grunting, growling and yammering. They could perhaps sharpen up their serenading skills. I highly recommend you go on the internet and watch an albatross courtship dance. It's sumptuous – like a well-rehearsed ballet – whilst their beak clacking sounds like a pneumatic drill (less sumptuous).

These dances are so elaborate and precise that albatrosses spend many years practising them before mating. The specificity of these rituals helps ensure partner recognition, so you don't accidentally cop off with the wrong albatross!

Laysan albatross climate crisis

As zoologist Lucy Cooke also pointed out, due to rising sea levels, the low-lying colony of albatross nests at Laysan could sadly be wiped out by 2050. However, by moving to new higher-ground colonies and raising chicks, these same-sex female pairs are helping to keep their species alive. These wonderful female Laysan albatrosses are doing it their way to help their species survive. How about a round of applause for the Laysan albatrosses?

 SUPER BONUS ALBATROSS FACT:

The name 'albatross' is believed to originally come from the Arabic word *al-ghattas* (translation is 'sea eagle'). The word came to English via the Spanish word *alcatraz*, which translates as 'gannet'.

> The Oxford English Dictionary tells us that the word *alcatraz* was originally applied by the English to the frigatebird. It could be that this then morphed into 'albatross' via the Latin for 'white' which is *alba* (frigatebirds are predominantly black, whilst albatrosses are white).

Seabirds and plastic waste

I want to end our look at the magnificent albatross with a look at their welfare. Of the 22 albatross species we have today, 15 are currently threatened with extinction. There are many factors causing this, but one is significantly harming the albatross and most other seabirds: plastic waste.

Studies have revealed a large amount of ingested plastic in dead seabird chicks. They cannot digest it. Many adult seabirds see plastic in the water and eat it, thinking it's food. The adults then regurgitate this plastic and feed it to their chicks. Many healthy chicks have died this way. It's a heart-breaking, painful image. And it's our fault.

It shocked me when I heard this and I hope it shocks you too. Please, please do your bit: don't leave your rubbish on the beach. And if you see rubbish or plastic on a beach or by a river, please pick it up – if you can – and dispose of it properly. Right now, seabirds everywhere, like the majestic Laysan albatrosses, really need our support. And they need it now.

Let's move on now to an animal that I'm confident most of us know. Or at least we think we know. It's time to say, '*Ciao!*' to the small fishy-horses that are doing life in their own particular way…

Seahorses

Seahorses are small marine fish that first emerged about 25 million years ago. They're found all over the world, in varied tropical and temperate areas including seagrass, mangroves, estuaries and coral reefs. They're known to live in the Pacific, the Atlantic, the Mediterranean... even the Thames estuary! In terms of the Thames estuary, I guess Canvey Island has the amusement arcades. Maybe seahorses are suckers for the 2p coin-pusher machines? Who knows.

What we do know for sure is that seahorses are strikingly beautiful and most whimsical in their appearance. They have their name because their heads and necks resemble the head and neck of a horse. Seahorses even have a snout that resembles a horse's muzzle. But the similarities with land-based horses ends with a seahorse's appearance. Seahorses don't eat polo mints and they aren't a cowboy's preferred mode of transport.

In terms of their size, seahorses can be tiny – 1.5cm – up to a less-than-tiny 35cm.

BONUS SEAHORSE FACTS:

Seahorses have an upright posture, a curly prehensile tail and bony body armour. This body armour is similar to an insect's exo-skeleton, protecting seahorses from predators.

Their upright posture when swimming means that seahorses aren't great movers. In fact, the dwarf seahorse

> is the slowest-moving fish in the world, with a top speed of
> 1.5m per hour. Because of their lack of swimming prowess,
> seahorses are more commonly spotted clasping onto a
> stationary object – like a rock – with their tail.

When brilliant marine biologist Dr Helen Scales joined us
on the show, she pointed out that there's a lot of mysticism
and folklore around seahorses, all linked to their striking horse-
like looks…

- Did you know that in ancient times, Greek fishermen
  would sometimes catch seahorses in their nets, believing
  them to be 'the tiny offspring of Poseidon's mighty steeds'?
  Maybe these same fishermen thought clam shells were
  pizza ovens for lobster's bungalows?

- Meanwhile, the Romans believed
  that seahorses were a cure for
  men going bald. They would mix
  together seahorse ashes, vinegar
  and goose fat, before smearing
  the mixture onto a balding head.
  I would suggest a more effective
  way for Romans to fight male
  baldness might have been to
  attach a number of seahorses
  directly to the scalp. Seahorse
  toupee, Brutus?

- Today, in China, people are known to hold seahorses during childbirth for good luck. I assume that's meant as good luck for the parents-to-be rather than the seahorse.

On that final note, it's worth acknowledging that seahorses have seen a drastic decline in their numbers. This has been caused primarily by habitat loss, by being caught in trawlers' nets and by a mammoth global trade. It's claimed that at least 25 million seahorses are traded every year for use in traditional Chinese medicine, in which seahorses are believed to help conquer impotence, asthma and skin infections. However, there's no evidence to back this up.

Seahorse smuggling is rampant and we know that populations around the world have fallen by between 30 and 50 per cent in recent years. As a consequence, 12 seahorse species have been declared 'vulnerable' (one step from being 'endangered') by the International Union for the Conservation of Nature. If we're to swing 'luck' back in favour of these incredible sea creatures, things need to change. People need to stop buying seahorses! It's really not cool.

Seahorse super-dads

The reason we're looking at seahorses through the Doing It My Way lens is because they have a sensational unique adaptation. You see, it's male seahorses – rather than females – that have evolved to look after the unborn young.

You're wondering, 'How does that work?' We were very lucky that Helen Scales was on hand to explain…

Let's talk seahorse sex!

It all starts – quelle surprise – with male seahorses 'fighting' for a female's attention. According to Amanda Vincent of marine conservation organisation Project Seahorse, males 'tail-wrestle' and snap their heads at each other (this behaviour will be familiar to anyone who's frequented Ritzy's nightclub in Ipswich on a Friday night). Once the males have had a good tail-wrestle and decided who's won, the female and the male champion come together for a mating dance.

To reproduce, the female first puts her eggs into the male, whilst the male fires his sperm into the sea. The fired sperm then enter the male's egg pouch and fertilise the eggs. The male gives nutrients to the eggs, via his egg pouch.

At the end of the gestation period, which can last between two and four weeks, the pregnant male's abdominal area begins to expand and contract. These contractions in the male then fire out between a dozen to 1,000 fully formed baby seahorses into the surrounding water. Meanwhile, the female is down the pub, sinking a few pornstar martini cocktails with the girls and playing darts. No, she's not: seahorses don't have access to pubs (or indeed restaurants) unless they have their Adult Seahorse ID (ASID).

Million-dollar question: why do seahorses reproduce this way?

Has it always been this way, or did male seahorses one day say to their partner, not really meaning it: 'Don't worry. I can look after the eggs for a bit. You go out with your friends. Go on, treat yourself.'?

In the absence of any proof to back up the above, the honest answer is we don't know for sure. Some scientists speculate that males have evolved to carry the young because it frees up females to prepare more eggs. The logic being that more baby seahorses being produced more quickly gives the species a greater chance of survival. There could be something in this, since only about five in every 1,000 baby seahorses survive to become adults.

The reason the seahorse survival rate is so low is because the babies – who are weak swimmers – are often carried away by ocean currents before they can hook their tail to a rock. This means they end up being eaten by other bigger fish and mammals. The odds really are stacked against these beautiful creatures. And it's not helped by humans catching more of them than can breed, in the quest to fight things like male impotence. As a species, we really can be massive bubbleheads.

With their progressive approach to reproduction, seahorses are a shining example of an animal 'doing it my way'. But seahorses aren't the only animals defying gender norms. There are plenty of other creatures doing their best to smash the patriarchy. So let's play a cheeky game of everyone's favourite quiz... **Binary Schminary**.

Here are some facts about animals defying gender norms. You have to decide if they're real or not...

1. **Slipper shell snails, known as crepidula, transition from male to female wherever a female in the group dies. Is that a real fact or not?**

ANSWER: **That's real!** It's called 'sequential hermaphroditism'. The snails change sex when they reach a certain size and depending on the sexes of the other slipper snails around. (Must be convenient to just change if there's not enough of one thing to go around.)

2. **True or false – female rhesus monkeys are disinterested in sex to the point where they only allow it once a year?**

ANSWER: **It's false!** Female rhesus monkeys have incredibly high sex drives, with the females objectifying the males, chasing them and doing pretty much everything else apart from actually forcing them to mate with them. When will *Planet of the Apes* get the all-female reboot we've been dreaming of?!

3.   **True or false – 40 per cent of male marsh harrier birds have evolved to resemble their female counterparts.**

ANSWER: **True!** Scientists believe the males have assumed a female appearance to prevent them from being attacked by other males. Personally I think it's for an elaborate *Mrs. Doubtfire*-type ruse for a harrier bird to see his kids again.

4.   **The male red-sided garter snake can smell like a female to trick other male snakes into trying to have sex with him. Is that real or bogus?**

ANSWER: **This is real!** To increase their odds of mating with the female, male garter snakes give off female pheromones, allow a swarm of fooled males to come towards them, and then sneak away to mate with the available female. Easily done – sometimes I think I'm in love with someone but then I realise that I just really enjoy their laundry detergent. Mmm, Surf Tropical Lily & Ylang Ylang, have mercy.

That's the end of this cheeky game of **Binary Schminary**.

I hope you've enjoyed learning about the incredible seahorse. These miraculous small wet ponies really need our support. They truly are a marvel of evolution.

It's time now to check out our final animal that's 'doing it their way'. Please go wild, go crazy for this very stupendous reptile...

Gecko

Geckos are small and – for the most part – carnivorous lizards. There are roughly 1,500 different types of gecko, living in warm climates all over the world. In terms of their size, they can range from 1.5cm in length up to 60cm. Oh and they happen to be brilliant! Here are some reasons why...

Different to many lizards, geckos tend to be nocturnal

Geckos have excellent night vision skills. In low light, a gecko's colour vision is 350 times more sensitive than human eyes. Which maybe explains why geckos are nocturnal... seeing a rainbow in daylight would be a psychedelic nightmare for a gecko.

On the subject of gecko vision, did you know that geckos don't have eyelids? Instead they have a transparent membrane covering each eye. If they get dirt on an eye, they'll lick the membrane, keeping it clean and moist. Imagine being able to lick your eye. Actually maybe don't...

Gobby geckos

Another thing that makes geckos stand out from other lizards is their phenomenal ability to vocalise. Some geckos can chirp or make clicking sounds, whilst others can hiss. On the show, I remember Sue telling the audience that a few years ago she was filming a TV show in Thailand with the mighty Liza Tarbuck. When Sue went to her room she could hear someone repeatedly shouting the word, 'Gecko! Gecko!' Sue thought it was Liza messing about, but it turned out it was a Tokay gecko calling its name!

If you go online and look for a Tokay gecko's call, you'll notice that it genuinely sounds like they're yelling, 'Gecko! Gecko!' I promise I'm not talking twaddle. It's very impressive and most amusing.

BONUS GECKO FACT:

Geckos (like many lizards) can choose to lose their tail as a defence against predators. That's right, geckos have decoy tails!

Here's how it works: when a predator grabs a gecko, the gecko can make its tail fall off. The tail will still be moving and twitching – which often distracts the predator – and enables the gecko to do a runner. Afterwards, geckos can regrow their tails, but they often grow back shorter... a small price to pay to survive another day.

Expert climbers

Geckos are marvels of climbing, thanks to their perfectly adapted feet. To skilfully cling and climb, many believe, is down to geckos having sticky toes. But it's more complicated than that. Geckos have lots of tiny nanoscale hairs, called 'setae'. Lining every toe, these tiny setae hairs become adhesive when pushed up against something solid. Each gecko has 6 million setae: enough to create sufficient force to support the weight of two humans. I respectfully ask that you don't test this theory by sitting on a gecko. It'll make quite a mess…

★ **SUPER BONUS GECKO FACT:**

As you know, we humans have two sets of teeth across our lifetime and that's it. Geckos on the other hand are what we call polyphyodonts. This is a fancy unpronounceable word that refers to animals who continually replace their teeth across their lifetime.

How this works is that geckos always have new teeth growing in their jaws, usually just behind the old teeth. A new tooth is then ready to move forward and take the place of the old tooth, when needed. This is similar to sharks' ability for teeth renewal, mentioned earlier in the book.

Geckos have a total of 100 teeth and can replace any of them every 4 months or so. I suggest that some brainbox please acts fast and soon develops the science so humans can also do this. Please! I can't afford the extortionate rates dentists charge!

As you can see, for many reasons, geckos are cool and amazing. But why have I chosen to put them into this Doing It My Way group? Simple: as zoologist and friend of the show Lucy Cooke explained, geckos are 'doing it their way' by reproducing asexually. Some gecko species lay eggs, some are live-bearing (giving birth to fully formed geckos rather than eggs) and others are asexual.

When it comes to asexual gecko species there are no males… just females. Lucy suggested this is a great example of males being evolutionary wastage! I'll leave you to make your minds up on that one. It got a good laugh from the audience…

So how do asexual geckos reproduce?

Lucy explained, taking mourning geckos as her example. The entire population is female. This means that female mourning geckos don't need males to produce their young. In fact, these geckos don't need to have sex at all.

Mourning geckos reproduce via parthenogenesis (virgin birth). What this means is that the eggs and young only have a mother; the gecko egg develops into an embryo without the need for male fertilisation. Female mourning geckos 'do it their way' by cloning themselves – rather than requiring her egg to be fertilised.

Every two to four weeks they look for a safe spot to lay and hide two more eggs. Across their whole lifetime – they typically live for around five years – a mourning gecko may lay 300 eggs. So, they lay their eggs and breed their clones. Mourning geckos are doing it their way and they're winning!

Asexual courtship

What's really interesting is that these all-female gecko populations still perform courtship behaviour before the eggs are laid. Two female geckos will form a bond, with one non-ovulating female taking on the male role and the other ovulating female taking the typical female role. This is known as female/female pseudocopulation: behaviour similar to copulation that serves a reproductive function, but without actual sexual union.

Gecko pseudocopulation involves the stimulation of both females' organs, but no actual sex. The eggs are laid and their chromosomes (DNA molecules) are identical to the single biological parent, hence geckos are cloning themselves. So these amazing tiny female lizards can climb up walls, have a lifetime of new teeth and replicate themselves. Not too shabby!

Before we say au revoir to this fabulous group that do life in their own way, I hope these three very different creatures – the albatross, the seahorse and the gecko – have opened your eyes to just how fluid gender can be in the animal kingdom.

Oh, there's just time for us to have a cheeky quick look at one last Doing It My Way creature... the **Stoplight Parrotfish**. Scientists have proven that this fish changes from female to male. You see, stoplight parrotfish live in groups of females with one single dominant male. If the male dies, then one of the females will change gender to assume the male role.

And not only that, but these parrotfish can also sleep for over ten hours at a time in cocoons of mucus. Sounds a bit too slimy for me. I think I'll stick with doing it my way: pillows and a duvet thank you very much...

BITESIZE NATURE TABLE

Time again now for some more ~~dad jokes~~ brilliant wildlife facts for you.

Did you know...?

Box jellyfish have no blood, no brains and no heart – just something to bear in mind if one pops up on Tinder.

The thorny prickly bramble – or blackberry – grows so fast it can travel along the ground 7.5cm a day, making it not only faster than Great Western Railway, but with a better buffet too.

Sloths only defecate once a week – expelling a third of their body weight, leaving them drained and vulnerable to attack. Which is why I keep a can of Red Bull and a flick-knife in the bathroom at all times.

In the mountains of eastern California, a Great Basin bristlecone pine tree is thought to be Earth's oldest living organism at more than 4,850 years. This is unbelievably impressive, but the old tree, unsurprisingly, has some outdated views... like thinking smoking is good for you.

THE MASTER BUILDERS

Walt Disney has been credited as saying, 'You can dream, create, design and build the most wonderful place in the world. But it requires people to make the dream a reality.' I'm sorry Mr Walt, but as much as I love *101 Dalmatians* and *The Jungle Book*, you've got this wrong. It doesn't require only *people* to build the most wonderful places in the world. As our look at this next group – nature's Master Builders – will demonstrate, there are plenty of animals who are supremely talented when it comes to building the most wonderful homes.

In fact, if there was an animal version of TV's *Grand Designs* (this is me officially pitching for such a show) then the two animals we're showcasing here would definitely feature.

Put your hard hat on as we greet our first wild titans of construction…

European Badgers

Short-legged and with stocky bodies, European badgers are powerfully built nocturnal mammals. They're also a joyous sight to behold. Before we focus on their skills as master builders, let me properly introduce you…

Living across Europe (the clue's in the name), European badgers have black and grey coats, with a distinctive black and white stripe on their head. They hail from the same family lineage as weasels and, just like weasels, they have a long, elongated head. Growing to between 70 and 90cm in length (roughly the size of a springer spaniel), European badgers can live up to 15 years in the wild.

Where does the name 'badger' come from?

We don't know for sure how badgers got their name. *The Oxford English Dictionary* suggests the name could date back to the 16th century and come from the word 'badge': a reference to the striking white mark on the head, which looks like a 'badge' or family crest.

However they've come by their name, European badgers are highly intelligent, handsome animals. Zoologist and badger fanatic Billy Heaney came on the show to talk us through the intriguing way badgers communicate with each other…

Talking badgers

Badgers communicate with one another through smells! I know this sounds weird, but it isn't completely surprising when you know that a badger's sense of smell is about 800 times sharper than our own.

In fact, badgers have many scent glands on their body, all producing an array of different smells. These contrasting whiffs alert other badgers to various warnings, as well as mating status. Who knew that pongs could have such meaning?

Badgers are social and live in a group, known as a clan or cete. It's common for each badger clan to share a particular scent or smell. This is so that everyone in the clan is immediately identifiable. The process by which a clan shares its unique odour has a name that's truly priceless. Badgers do what scientists refer to as 'bum pressing'.

'Bum pressing'? Seriously?!

I've not it made up. 'Bum pressing' is real.

As Billy Heaney explained, all badgers have a scent gland under their tail and above their bottom. 'Bum pressing' occurs when a clan's dominant male – known as a boar – places his bum directly onto another clan member's bum. The dominant male proceeds to press his scent gland directly onto the other badger's scent gland. What follows is a rhythmic bum-pressing or bum-rubbing procedure. Cheeky badgers.

The dominant boar 'presses bums' with the entire clan, so that everyone has the same unique smell. This means that if a stray badger enters the clan with a differently scented bum, the clan will pose serious questions to the stranger via the medium of smell or indeed claw.

So, that's badgers' bum pressing. You're very welcome.

Let's now focus on why European badgers are such accomplished master builders…

Badger setts

Badgers live in incredibly elaborate underground chambers –
usually located in woods – known as setts. These subterranean
chambers are dug by the badgers who, thanks to their strong
claws and muscly snouts, are phenomenal diggers. The holes
that badgers dig can be 60–280cm deep and often 30–60cm
in diameter. I don't know about you, but I'm feeling a new
direction for the *Mission Impossible* films. A new spin-off action
spy series, featuring a crack field team of badgers led by Ethan

Badger... *Badgers Impossible!* They
have 30 seconds to un-detonate a
carrot! Come on! Who's in? It
literally writes itself!

Badger setts can be huge.
I mentioned earlier that most
badgers live in a clan. Clans
usually include four to eight
adults, spending up to 70 per
cent of their lives underground.

The largest badger-built setts
are big enough to accommodate multiple badger families: 15
or more animals. These larger setts have been known to feature
300m of tunnels, multiple chambers and as a many as 50
entrances. With a home this big, the vast number of entrances
obviously includes things like a tradesman's entrance for when
a badger electrician has to be called in to fix the sett's dated
wiring. There will of course also be 'a grand entrance' for when
foreign dignitaries stay, and a secret entrance for emergencies
(like when a badger has to rush out and buy more schnapps).

But as impressive as the 50 or so entrances of a badger's sett are, badgers are such clever builders that they even construct themselves a latrine of leaves and dried grass *outside* the sett. It turns out that badgers are meticulously clean animals – how civilised!

And before you ask, not all badger setts are new-builds. Many badger setts in the UK are 100 years old – like stately homes (and with the same lax approach to inheritance tax). In northeastern Germany there is a badger sett that has been in use for over ten thousand years! Thankfully, these older setts are passed down through generations (otherwise, it's near impossible for millennial badgers to get on the badger property market).

BONUS BADGER FACT:

When it comes to building creature comforts for their setts, badgers are absolute artists. In addition to the latrines I just mentioned, badgers also make themselves bedding out of grass, straw and leaves, which they change and freshen up on a daily basis.

So, as you now know, badgers are master builders. Their setts can be huge: featuring hundreds of metres of tunnels with lots of chambers for sleeping and rearing young. But badgers aren't the only creatures to get their *Grand Designs* on. To find out more, let's play a quick game of **Who'd Live in a House Like This?**

I'm going to tell you about some impressive animal house-building – and you have to decide if it's true – or utterly without foundation.

Here's the first one...

1.   Beavers not only build dams, but within those dams they create individual lodges for beaver families and can work on them for up to 20 years. True or false?

ANSWER: **True!** Though the average beaver dam is around 2 x 1.5m – the largest on record was around 850m wide. It's basically like Center Parcs, only with less crazy golf and more wood-gnawing.

2.   Moles always dig their tunnels in triangular grids – throughout which there is a one-way system in place, so the moles never have to pass each other. True or false?

ANSWER: **This is false!** Moles aren't beholden to geometry like maths teachers or the population of Milton Keynes.

3.   How about this – cathedral termites build towers over 4.5m high out of mud, chewed wood, saliva and faeces. These cathedrals also spread underground for several acres – where the termites keep little gardens of fungi that they grow and use to feed themselves. True or false?

ANSWER: **This is true!** The termites actually live in the underground area – using the towers to give them the shelter and humidity they need to thrive – and to show off to their neighbours in the bungalow next door.

4.   How about this? Weaver birds build nests large enough for 400 of them to live in together, with their own security systems to keep out intruders. True or false?

ANSWER: **This too is true!** Known as the 'sociable weaver' bird, they make the biggest nests of any bird. These can remain occupied for over 100 years. The nests have separate areas for each breeding pair of birds. And the entrances are protected by spiky sticks to keep out unwanted visitors. An idea you may want to embrace for your next home.

5. And finally... catfish pile up riverbed mud into shallow underwater dams. They do this as a shelter against the water current, similar to putting a windbreaker up on the beach (only with less chance it'll immediately be blown over onto your packed lunch). True or false?

ANSWER: **This is sadly false.** Though catfish do burrow into the ground to make little caves for the female to lay their eggs. Or for some peace and quiet as they attempt to impersonate other people online.

I hope you enjoyed that game. You now know that lots of animals are amazing builders. Before we move on to our next in-depth look at a master builder, here's a final charming badger fact for you...

★ **SUPER BONUS CHARMING BADGER FACT:**

Did you know that badgers are partial to a supper of baked beans and macaroni cheese? This is the exact meal that Badger prepared for Ratty and Mole in *The Wind in the Willows*, just before The Battle for Toad Hall. This proves what great taste badgers have. Time for a TV badger cookery show, methinks. Anyone for an episode of *The Great British Badger Off*?

Let's leave the badgers to their baked bean and macaroni feast and meet our next virtuoso of the animal construction world. These master builders may be a lot smaller than the European badger, but they're just as impressive...

Leaf-cutter Ants

Found in the rainforests of Central and South America – and measuring around 0.6cm long – leaf-cutter ants are small in stature. But when it comes to their talent for construction these ants are IMMENSE. Leaf-cutter ant colonies can house up to 10 million ants (at the time of writing this, that's bigger than the entire population of London, which is 9.6 million).

The sheer size and complexity of leaf-cutter ant nests and societies is rivalled only by humans. But first...

What's with the name?

Leaf-cutter ants are so-called because of their unique chainsaw-like mandibles (jaws). These mandibles easily cut leaves and foliage into manageable pieces to carry, and serve as a very handy tool for their building work.

So why are leaf-cutter ants master builders?

The esteemed Dr Claire Asher, with her PhD specialising in ants, joined us on the show and shared the home-making genius of leaf-cutter ants...

The story of leaf-cutter ants as master builders starts when a new queen leaf-cutter ant is born. Soon after her birth, the young queen leaves the nest and takes a piece of the nest's fungus with her (more on the fungus later!). Walking out with the fungus, the queen heads forth to start her own nest.

Before we move on with the story, let me tell you about leaf-cutter ants' nests. They're truly staggering. Leaf-cutter ant nests – found in rainforest or woodland – are massive. They can be up to 15.2m across (the equivalent of three large SUVs back to back) and 4.9m deep. Remember, these ants are only about 0.6cm long!

Clearly, these giant nests aren't something the queen can just knock up herself in the space of an hour, like pitching a tent. To construct these nests is a technical achievement akin to the Egyptians building the pyramids. The queen leaf-cutter needs help! Back to the story...

Time to call in the professionals

When the young leaf-cutter queen leaves her birth nest, a large team of worker ants joins her and starts building an elaborate new nest for her (NB you can always identify worker ants by the fact they always have a pencil behind their ear. They also shake their head and tut a lot).

Each ant fills a specific role in the construction and maintenance of the new nest. There are workers (builders), soldiers (to protect the nest), rubbish collectors (to keep the nest clean and tidy) and the egg-laying queen (to produce more ants).

Leaf-cutter ant nests are so vast and complicated that – as they build them – the worker ants leave scent trails to help them find their way back home.

More than just master builders

As Claire Asher explained, what's even more mind-blowing about leaf-cutter ants is that they aren't just master builders. Did you know that they're also the world's first farmers? Leaf-cutter ants actually learned to farm 50 million years ago: way before humans.

What do leaf-cutter ants farm?

Remember I mentioned earlier that when a queen leaf-cutter is born, she leaves her birth-nest taking a bit of fungus with her?

When she starts her new colony and the massive intricate nest is being built by her construction team, everyone needs food. And this is where the fungus comes into play. Leaf-cutter ants eat fungus.

Fungus garden

There are 10 million ants in a colony – is there enough fungus to keep everyone going? There certainly is, and the reason why is incredible…

At the same time the worker ants are building the new massive nest, they're also building an enormous dedicated fungus garden. The small bit of fungus that the queen originally brought with her is placed in the fungus garden and the worker ants start taking leaves to the fungus, to feed the fungus and help it grow. Et voilà! Leaf-cutter ants are farmers! Ingenious!

BONUS LEAF-CUTTER ANT FACT:

Leaf-cutter ants can carry pieces of leaves to feed the fungus that are almost 50 times the weight of the ant. This is the equivalent of a small man called Derek carrying a car with his bare hands!

In return for being fed by the ants, the fungus returns the favour. There is a positive symbiotic relationship here between the ants and the fungus. The ants feed the fungus and, in return, the fungus produces edible growths that the ants can eat. The fungus and ants are dependent on one another: the fungus is unable to live outside the nest and the ants will die without the fungus... hence they build a special garden for the fungus. So not only are leaf-cutter ants master builders, but they're also fantastic farmers! Go leaf-cutter ants! YOU ROCK!

★ SUPER BONUS LEAF-CUTTER ANT FACT:

So, leaf-cutter ants are expert builders and farmers. But did you know that they're also skilled pharmacists?! Here's how...

Leaf-cutter ants protect the all-important fungus from hazardous microbes (which could infect the fungus). The ants protect the fungus with antibiotic-forming bacteria that they carry on their bodies. This bacteria stops any microbes from harming the fungus.

So effective are the ants at protecting the fungus, scientists are now looking to apply this bacteria to human pharmaceuticals! Builders, farmers and pharmacists... I don't know about you, but I'm thinking of voting leaf-cutter ant at the next general election.

So, there you have it: leaf-cutter ants are masters of three trades: building, farming and pharmacist-ing! (I'm not convinced that last one's a word, but go with it). Sadly though, leaf-cutter ants make lousy accountants as they're no good at maths and – let's be honest – calculators are too big for them.

BONUS LEAF-CUTTER ANT FACT:

Remember, how this story started with the young queen leaving her nest, taking a bit of fungus with her and going on an adventure to start a new community?

Leaf-cutter ant queens can live an astonishing 20 years and be around 5cm long (this is big for a leaf-cutter). In her lifetime, the queen may produce between 150 to 200 million baby ants. Each leaf-cutter colony has only one queen; and the queen is the only ant in the nest capable of reproduction. Make no mistake: leaf-cutter queens are the boss!

So leaf-cutter queen ants are mighty impressive. But what do you know about other queens of nature? Let's find out, as we play a game I like to call **Animal or Diva?** Because that's its name.

In this game, I'm going to tell you a fact about a royal. You have to tell me if you think it's a queen animal of its species, or an actual human royal.

1. **This royal killed all the other potential royals to ensure they took the throne and then demanded to be fed on a high-sugar liquid diet by their nurse. Animal or diva?**

ANSWER: **That's an animal. In fact it's a queen bee,** who once hatched, will kill her unhatched rivals and then be fed throughout her life on royal jelly provided by nurse bees. I believe that's also Jacob Rees-Mogg's backstory.

2. **This royal insists all underlings have a musky substance sprayed on them before entering the royal space. Animal or diva?**

ANSWER: **That's a diva! It was French King Louis XIV.** During his reign in the 17th century many people thought water was spreading disease so stopped bathing. To hide the stench, Louis had everyone sprayed head to toe in a fragrance. He even had a different scent, designed just for him, for every day of the week!

3.   **OK, this royal keeps a tight rein on the number of her subjects by only allowing them to reproduce when she wants them to.**

ANSWER: **This is a termite queen!** Termite queens release a pheromone around the colony that can block the reproductive capabilities of all the other termites. Then when she dies, the pheromone stops. Isn't nature fun?!

4.   **OK, last one. Every morning, this royal coats themselves in white lead ore, vinegar and sometimes arsenic, hydroxide, carbonate and part of an egg...**

ANSWER: **That one's actually Queen Elizabeth I!** Every morning she'd coat her face with lead, arsenic, egg whites and a whole host of other toxic chemicals. Still, can't be worse than one of those Aztec clay masks you get off Amazon.

THE MASTER BUILDERS

That's the end of this game of **Animal or Diva** and indeed our look at nature's master builders.

Remember, the next time you need that extension built or a roof fixing, who are you gonna call? That's right! The Badger and Leaf-cutter Ant Construction Company. *(Terms and conditions apply. Badgers and Leaf-cutter Ant builders cannot be held liable for acts of god – or indeed acts of weasels – against your new extension and/or roof.)*

BITESIZE NATURE TABLE

Before we check out our next supergroup, let me share
some amazing bizarre natural world facts with you.

Did you know...?

Prairie dogs often greet each other by kissing.
This is not – as I recently found out – a legal defence when
you're discovered in a safari park at 4am.

Neuroscientists studying how the brain analyses speech
have trained rats to recognise the difference between
Japanese and Dutch. Scientists believe it's to do with the
natural rhythm of the languages. It also explains why rats
have such a penchant for tulip tempura.

Galapagos tortoises take 30 years to reach puberty,
but after that they really start to come out of their shells.

During copulation, a male honeybee's penis turns inside
out and snaps off, leaving the bee to die.
Luckily, with humans this only happens metaphorically.

THE POWER PLANTS

It's now time to meet a group I'm calling The Power Plants. I appreciate 'power' is an unusual choice of word when discussing plants. It sounds like I'm trying to grab your interest by giving a Marvel-movie-makeover to flora. Either that or I'm pitching an underwhelming plant-based spin-off of the *Power Rangers*. It's honestly neither of those. There's a legitimate reason for the name of this group.

Many people's go-to impression of plants is that they don't do much. They just sit there, taking in the sun, needing to be watered. Like my sweet Uncle George. Don't ask. We tend to think plants aren't as exciting or as cool as animals. Do you know a plant that can spin around a wheel, ask 'Who's a pretty boy?' or bring you your newspaper? No you don't. Plants are boring.

However, I'm confident that this power plants group will show you that plants are way more kick-ass than we give them credit for. Plants are powerful in the way they live and survive. And as you're about to discover, plants have directly impacted the way we live our lives today. So, buckle up and prepare to be bedazzled. Come on! Let's go...

Amazonian Giant Water Lily

I know what you're thinking. I've just used words like 'kick-ass' and 'bedazzled' and I've opened with a water lily. In which idiot's universe is a water lily kick-ass? Has the author lost his mind? No, I haven't. And before this inner reflection by the author (that's me) becomes any weirder, here's why the Amazonian giant water lily merits its place in the... Pantheon of Power Plants...

Native to South America, the Amazonian giant water lily is absolutely massive. It has a very big round leaf – often referred to as a 'pad'. These pads can grow to be a giant 3m wide, float on water and are strong enough to support the weight of a small child! Or your money back...

BONUS AMAZONIAN GIANT WATER LILY FACT:

This giant water lily is a proper power plant when it comes to defending itself. On the underside of the lily's enormous pads are sharp spines that defend the plant from herbivore fish.

But as impressive as the Amazonian giant water lily is, I need to make a confession. Despite its grand title, it's only the world's *second* largest water lily. For a long time the 3m Amazonian giant water lily was believed to be the largest, until a swine Bolivian water lily at La Rinconada Gardens in Bolivia was recorded with a leaf size of 3.2m. Damn you Bolivian water lily!

So why tell us about the second-largest water lily? Who cares about second best?

Let me answer with a rhetorical question…

Remember when I asked for your opinion? Me neither. BOOM! Mic drop!

That's not it. Wrong rhetorical question. Here's what I meant to write…

It may be the world's second-largest water lily, but what would you say if I told you that the Amazonian giant water lily has revolutionised how we humans live our lives?

As genius ethnobotanist James Wong explained when he came on the show, the Amazonian giant water lily has completely transformed modern architecture. It's truly a power plant and it has an astonishing story to tell…

Today, our planet's super rich – you know, the irritating handful of people who own everything – are ploughing their entire fortunes into things like space travel. But 200 years ago, the super rich were obsessed with things closer to home: specifically, plants. The mega wealthy in Victorian times were all about discovering new exotic plants, bringing them back to the UK and keeping them alive so they could display them to the world (and show them off to other mega-wealthy Victorians in the process).

So, in the 19th century, there began an exotic plant rivalry between very wealthy people. When it came to the Amazonian giant water lily, it was all about the Duke of Devonshire versus the Duke of Northumberland. Both were vying to be the first to successfully cultivate this massive lily and have it bloom in the UK. Some seeds were brought to England in 1849 (indeed, the Latin name for the lily is *Victoria amazonica*: named after Queen Victoria) and the contest began. A lot of money was invested by both dukes to try to replicate the climate of the Amazon rainforest.

There were two main issues to overcome: first, you had to replicate the lily's warm, damp, swampy environment (not easy in a Victorian winter with no modern central heating). Second, these lilies grow 40cm every day and up to 3m in diameter. So you needed to create a building large enough to house them. But also a building without pillars, where people could visit and see the full majesty of these enormous lilies without walls obstructing the view. Therefore, what was required was a building that had a glass ceiling for light and warmth, but that was also pillarless. At the time, no one knew how to construct such a building.

Enter Joseph Paxton

Joseph Paxton was a Victorian architect, engineer, MP and – crucially – keen gardener. It was Paxton, working for the Duke of Devonshire at his glasshouse in Chatsworth, who first noticed that these giant lilies were strong enough to take the weight of a small child (even though the pad is only millimetres thick). Indeed, the *Illustrated London News* (the world's first illustrated weekly news magazine) published a picture of Paxton's daughter Annie sitting on a giant lily pad.

Paxton figured out that the lily pad's great strength comes from the tough reinforced veins that run along and across the underside of the leaf. The veins effectively act as girders, supporting great weight. It turns out, the Amazonian giant water lily is an incredible feat of natural engineering!

Taking inspiration from (which is posh for copying) the design of the giant lily's leaf, Paxton designed and built a glasshouse at Chatsworth capable of growing the lily. On 14 November 1849, the first flower opened and the contest between the two dukes was over. And so, the solution of how to build a large pillarless glasshouse big and light enough for the giant water lily to thrive, came from the giant water lily's own leaf design! It was a complete revolution in architecture.

After the great success at Chatsworth with the giant lily, Paxton was chosen to be the architect of the Great Exhibition of 1851 at Crystal Palace. At 563m long and 124m wide, Crystal Palace was four times the size of St Peter's Basilica in Rome. Again, Paxton's design for this vast glass structure was inspired by the leaf architecture of the Amazonian giant water lily. As James Wong pointed out to us, this same construction design can be seen all over the world today in airports, concert halls and shopping centres. Most buildings that are largely pillarless have Paxton's design – inspired by the giant water lily – to thank. Make no mistake: the Amazonian giant water lily is a proper legitimate kick-ass power plant.

So, we've learned that the giant water lily was the inspiration for the Great Exhibition's Crystal Palace in 1851. It turns out that technology often takes inspiration from the natural world. Did you know that Velcro was inspired by a dirty dog? Or that geckos are helping humans glue themselves to walls? Let's find out more about biomimicry in a game of **Glue or False**.

I'm going to give you an example of engineers 'borrowing' from nature, and you're going to tell me if you think it's true: biomimicry, or false: biomyth.

1. **Let's begin. True or false – due to its strength, spider silk has been used to make bulletproof vests.**

ANSWER: **That's true!** Spider silk is one of the toughest fibres in the natural world. It's stronger by weight than steel but also very flexible: the material equivalent of Jean-Claude Van Damme.

2. **How about this? True or false – Japanese engineers were inspired by kingfishers to design the bullet train.**

ANSWER: **This is also true!** High-speed trains don't yet have wings. But the Japanese Shinkansen bullet train has a nose shaped like a kingfisher's beak. Which reduces noise, cuts power use and makes the train go faster – and it can also skewer a 3-m-long stickleback.

3. **Here's another one: True or false – the Gherkin skyscraper in London is not only named after a pickled cucumber, but its entire structural integrity is based on one, too.**

ANSWER: **This is false.** Biomimicry was used in the Gherkin's design, but no pickles were harmed in the making of this landmark. In fact, the Gherkin has an external lattice structure based on a sponge called 'Venus' flower basket'. It forms part of a ventilation system that cuts the need for air conditioning in half. Although, just like a gherkin, I'd probably pick it off if anyone put a skyscraper on my burger.

4.   **And how about this one? True or false – beaver fur has inspired a hairy wetsuit.**

ANSWER: **Amazingly, this is true.** Beavers' fur traps warm pockets of air, which keeps them both warm and dry. This has inspired engineers at the Massachusetts Institute of Technology (MIT) to create a wetsuit described as a 'rubbery, fur-like pelt' for surfers. Sadly, the beaver suit isn't yet available to buy. Dam it!

5.   **And finally – there is a type of paint based on an elephant's breath. True or false?**

ANSWER: **This is false,** though Elephant's Breath is a Farrow & Ball colour. A kind of dull grey. However, there is a paint based on the lotus flower, the petals of which are covered in tiny little nails that repel dust and dirt. A German company spent four years developing a lotus-inspired paint that stays clean of dirt and dust. But no word on whether you can get it in the Farrow & Ball shade 'Dead Salmon'.

That's the end of **Glue or False**. We've learned a lot about biomimicry from that game. We've also learned that scientists and engineers are a load of old plagiarist 'tea leaves' (that's a botany term).

And that's us done looking at the Amazonian giant water lily. But before we move to our next power plant, let me end this bit with this…

Oscar Wilde once said that imitation is the sincerest form of flattery. On that basis, I hope you see just how awesome and inspiring plants can be for us humans. Let's face it, thanks to the Amazon giant water lily we now know how to build giant shopping centres! That's a positive, right?

I'm certain that the next power plant we're looking at will squash – once and for all – any thoughts you have about plants being boring. Our next plant is stunningly beautiful, but also ruthlessly deadly…

Tropical Pitcher Plant

A devilishly handsome plant predator, the tropical pitcher plant is a carnivore (meat eater). Around the world, there are approximately 630 species of carnivorous plants that we know about. In terms of tropical pitcher plants, there are roughly 170 species. They're mostly native to Southeast Asia, but are also found in northern Australia and Madagascar.

Many tropical pitcher plants feed on insects. But other species can catch larger meals including lizards, frogs, rodents and even small birds! Which begs the question…

A *Housefly* BUZZES in the Key of F

What did the tropical pitcher plant say to the waiter?

I'll have the cheeseburger with flies.

But how does a static tropical pitcher plant hunt, catch and eat an animal?

Tropical pitcher plants have evolved all sorts of leafy traps and snares to entice and attract their prey, before killing and eating them.

But to show you how they hunt, kill and eat their prey, we first need to talk you through the tropical pitcher plant in more detail. The very excellent Dr Chris Thorogood, head of science at the Oxford Botanic Garden & Arboretum, came on the show to enlighten us about these remarkable power plants...

The plant itself is nothing out of the ordinary – it's a vine-like plant. The stem can climb up to an impressive 15m tall. But it's on the very tips of the plant's leaves that things get interesting. The leaves' tips grow tendrils (a thread-like strand) off which a bell-shaped 'pitcher' grows and hangs. The 'pitcher' or 'cup' holds fluid.

The pitcher plant that Chris showed us had a pitcher that resembled a see-through ice-cream cone with a beautiful ornate fan over the top. Chris suggested that the ornate fan serves as a striking 'come hither' element, enticing insects towards the pitcher. So, the gaudy fan lures unsuspecting insects to the pitcher, which is effectively the plant's stomach. You can see where this is going...

The top rim of the pitcher is shiny and ornate – again, it's designed to appeal to potential prey. Crucially, the rim is also slippery (in a moustache-twirling villain kind of way). And as a whole, tropical pitcher plants have a sugary nectar smell, a smell that's irresistible to insects and beckons them. So that's the set-up...

How the plant gets its meal...

The pitcher produces a sweet smell that draws in insects. The insects teem around the top of the pitcher, having a yummy sugary snack off it. But remember, the moustache-twirling pitcher has a slippery rim. This oily rim causes insects to fall and aquaplane down into the pitcher (like a waterslide, but less fun and with no souvenir shop at the bottom). The insects fall inside the pitcher (the plant's stomach) and find themselves stuck at the bottom, in a soup of digesting fluid. Still think plants are dull?

The fluid in the pitcher is gooey with the texture of liquid honey. As the insect tries to escape, the sticky fluid draws it back down to the base of the pitcher. But even if the insect is as fierce as *The Hunger Games*' Katniss Everdeen and manages to climb up the pitcher's tube, the pitcher has yet another dastardly trick up its sleeve...

The wall of the pitcher's interior is covered in a surface of wax, which means an insect's claws get stuck. There's no escape and the insect drowns... before being dissolved by digestive enzymes and eaten. This is Bond villain-level skulduggery – a literal honey trap! Victory to the rogue power pitcher plants!

Why do tropical pitcher plants do this?

Do tropical pitcher plants *need* to eat meat or is this simply a lifestyle choice? Are they desperate to bulk up, so they can enter the World's Strongest Plant competition, pulling a jumbo jet with their bare leaves? What's this really all about? Why are tropical pitcher plants carnivores?

The answer is simple: most plants absorb the nutrients they need via their roots, absorbing nutrients from the soil. But tropical pitcher plants grow in places where the soil doesn't contain the nutrients they need. So they've had to adapt into carnivores to survive. As the plant breaks the insects down, so it absorbs the nitrogen it needs to live.

And as if this form of survival isn't cunning enough, Chris shared something even more astonishing...

On Mount Kinabalu in Borneo, there's a very special pitcher plant – the *Nepenthes rajah*. Growing high up on remote mountain slopes, there aren't enough insects for the plants to feed on. As a result, the Kinabalu pitcher plant has an alternative way of getting the nitrogen and nutrients it needs: it feeds on the faeces of local shrews. That's right: they eat shrew poo. *Délicieux*!

How does a plant eat an animal's poo? Is cutlery involved?

The Kinabalu pitcher plant grows a pitcher that resembles a slipper and can be up to 40cm long. The local tree shrews, a bit like squirrels, dangle from branches and gorge on the pitcher plant's syrupy nectar. Even though the pitcher's rim is slippery, the shrew doesn't fall in because it's hanging from a branch and has a good grip.

So, the shrew finishes drinking from the pitcher, but the plant has had no meal. However – and this is the clever bit – the pitcher's lid has adapted itself to be the perfect shape and size for a shrew's bum. So once the shrew has fed on the sweet, sweet nectar, it parks its bum on the lid and poos directly into the pitcher, using it as a toilet. The plant digests the nutrient-rich poo and both parties have had their lunch!

How brilliant is that? This is a serious mic drop moment for these incredible plants.

The final twist – if indeed we need another – is that occasionally the shrew can slip into the pitcher and the pitcher digests the shrew – as well as its poo. It's rare, but this can happen. Definitely cause at that point for the pitcher to get out the Rennies.

So that's our look at the fascinating, wonderful bloodthirsty pitcher plants. A 100 per cent bona fide power plant and it's not to be trifled with. Damn, I love trifle. The way that the jelly at the bottom marries perfectly with the custard layer and the light sponge cake that somehow manages to be soaked but not soggy...

Our next power plant demonstrates its mighty chutzpah in a very different way. Steeped in folklore and known for its medicinal and mind-bending properties, let's say a big 'Hi and hello!' to the...

Mandrake

What exactly is a mandrake?

Found across the Mediterranean and the Himalayas, mandrake is a herbaceous plant. It has purple flowers and yellow poisonous fruit. But the mandrake's legendary, magical status stems not from the plant, but its thick root beneath. The parsnip-like root can often resemble the human form and has hallucinogenic properties. What larks!

Mandrake root is such an effective narcotic that it can put us humans into a state of unconsciousness (at least if you consume enough – and don't be trying this at home). It's so effective as a narcotic that it was used as a surgical anaesthetic in ancient times. Mandrake is a power plant with a long history.

How did mandrake become so prominent in ancient times?

It's well documented that mandrake was popular with the Romans, Greeks and ancient Middle Eastern cultures.

But to explain why this plant became so noteworthy – and steeped in mystery – I need to tell you about the Doctrine of Signatures (DOS). Again, the very brilliant and knowledgeable Dr Chris Thorogood guested on the show and explained all…

The DOS dates back to ancient Greece. It states that any herbs or plants that resemble parts of the body can be employed by herbalists to treat ailments of those specific body parts. So if a plant looks like an ear, its job is to help soothe earache or cure deafness. As eccentric as this logic sounds today, the doctrine was given further credence by botanists in the 1600s. The botanists stated that the doctrine was correct because God clearly wanted to show man what plants would be useful for.

In terms of a mandrake, the dug-up root resembles a human body. This meant that botanists and scientists believed mandrake was a dedicated medicine for our bodies... simple as that. So, because it resembles the human body, mandrake root was used to make sleeping potions and ancient anaesthetics.

It won't surprise you that today, the Doctrine of Signatures is considered to be pseudoscience (a theory that claims to be scientific but isn't).

BONUS MANDRAKE FACT:

As you now know, a mandrake's root often resembles the human body. But sometimes the root can take – let me delicately say – a rather suggestive form! As a result, the ancient Greeks thought mandrake was also an aphrodisiac. Sadly, not true.

In ancient times, mandrake was believed to contain a demon

So, because it has such a mind-bending hallucinogenic effect on us, people were scared of mandrake. They believed the plant contained demons. As Chris Thorogood pointed out, if you pulled a mandrake directly out of the ground, people expected to hear a demon's deathly scream. Then the demon would move from the plant into your body and you would die.

To solve this problem of the demon leaving the plant and then killing the digger, people would dig around the mandrake's root until it was exposed. Then a dog would be tied to the root.

The person who tied the dog walks away and the dog tries to follow its owner. The dog pulls the root out of the ground, the demon screams, passes into the dog and the dog dies suddenly. After this the root could be handled without fear! I would suggest it's possible the people coming up with this ingenious workaround were perhaps getting high on their own mandrake supply.

 SUPER BONUS MANDRAKE FACT:

In the past, mandrake was also known as 'Crazy Apple' and 'Satan's Testicles'. As a result, it was made into amulets to bring good fortune and cure sterility.

Military mandrake

Another interesting fact about mandrake – helping to make it a power plant – is that it's been weaponised throughout history.

Around 200 BC, celebrity elephant-herder Hannibal had his troops infuse wine with mandrake root. They then pretended to retreat, leaving the wine for the attacking army to drink in celebration. Which they did, and in the process became so ill that Hannibal defeated them easily.

If we dig into this further, it turns out that animals and plants have been deadly to many historical figures. So much so that we've written a game about it, called **Now That's Tragic!**

I want to know from you, are the following nature-related deaths... **Tragic or false?**

1. **Here's the first one: In 1703 Hannah Twynnoy, a barmaid in Wiltshire, was killed by a tiger while working in a pub. Tragic or false?**

ANSWER: **It's tragic!** Poor Hannah was the first person in Britain to be killed by a tiger. She worked in a pub called the White Lion, which often had live exotic animals on display – never a good idea...

2. **How about this one? Roman Emperor Antoninus Pius died after eating a pudding of poisonous berries. Tragic or false?**

ANSWER: **It's false!** Antoninus Pius actually enjoyed a long, peaceful reign before he died in AD 161, after supposedly eating a huge amount of cheese. I'm rather concerned that's possible. Can any scientists reading this look into it for me?

3. **And what about this? Alexander I of Greece was murdered by a monkey. Is that tragic or false?**

ANSWER: **It's tragic!** It happened in 1920. Alexander was trying to break up a fight between a Barbary macaque monkey and his German shepherd dog when another monkey attacked him. And people said *Planet of the Apes* was unbelievable.

4. **And finally... The ancient Greek tragedian Aeschylus was killed by a tortoise. Tragic or false?**

ANSWER: **That's tragic!** History records that an eagle dropped a tortoise on Aeschylus's head. Eagles sometimes drop tortoises on rocks to crack their shells. All I can say is, for that ancient Greek tortoise, it was a sad end to an illustrious racing career. A classics joke for you there – don't ever tell me this book isn't highbrow.

THE POWER PLANTS

So that's our look at this wonderful group. Three very different and uniquely powerful plants. One with the strength to revolutionise modern architecture, despite being only millimetres thick. The second, a fiendish carnivore that can change its diet when required. And finally, a powerful narcotic plant that has us under its spell. In their very different ways, these three plants are hard as nails. So, the next time you walk through a garden, a meadow or rainforest, remember to be careful: there are badass plants everywhere.

Remember: plants are just as impressive as animals. They just don't make a big song and dance about it!

BITESIZE NATURE TABLE

Before we check out our next *Nature Table* group, here are some more snack-size *Nature Table* facts for you.

Did you know...?

The tarantula hawk wasp has one of the planet's most painfully irritating stings. The other is married to Trudie Styler.

Tulip bulbs were so valuable in 17th century Holland, they were used as currency.
The downside was that they regularly jammed the coin slots on supermarket trollies.

The easiest way to tell a crocodile and alligator apart is to take a close look at them when their mouths are closed.
If only the upper teeth are visible, it's an alligator.
If both sets are visible, it's a crocodile.
And if you take a close look when their mouths are open, it doesn't matter – because you're about to become dinner.

Acorns are poisonous to humans, which makes you wonder: why are the squirrels hoarding them and what are they planning?

ANIMAL
MAGNETISM

It's now that time in the book where we dim the lights, put some romantic music on – maybe a bit of Mr Barry White, aka the 'Walrus of Love' – pour ourselves a couple of espresso martinis and take a peek at a group I've named Animal Magnetism.

I hope my unsubtle intro and this title have already spelled it out. But if you're somehow still in the dark, with this group we're focusing on the birds and the bees. Actually, scrub that: there's no mention of birds or bees in this group. What I'm trying to say, in my inept way, is that this group is all about animal courtship.

The first animal we're looking at in this group doesn't exactly scream *Romeo and Juliet*. If I'm honest, I can't think of any animals that can actually scream 'Romeo and Juliet'. I've seen a cat online howling the words 'Oh Long Johnson' but I think it was about to throw up...

Anyway, let's take a look at some very well-known, surprisingly romantic creatures…

Earthworms

The words 'earthworms' and 'passion' may feel like unlikely partners, but let me assure you, worms have a stormy tale of courtship to tell.

But before we talk earthworm erotica, let's open with some initial facts…

- **There are approximately 3,000 species of earthworm worldwide.**
  Earthworms are invertebrates (an animal without a backbone. *See also*, most UK politicians working today).

- **Found all over the world, earthworms are smooth-skinned worms.**
  Earthworms have a head, tail and soft tube-like body. An earthworm's digestive system runs along the full length of its body.

- **Living in soil, earthworms can eat a variety of organic matter.**
  They eat plant matter, fungi, bacteria, nematodes and other micro-organisms. This makes earthworms a gardener's best friend; chomping and decomposing organic matter, keeping our soil fertile.

- **Did you know that earthworms breathe through their skin?**
  Air permeates an earthworm's skin by dissolving on the mucus that covers a worm's body. As air is taken in via the skin, so oxygen is drawn directly into the worm's circulatory system. The worm's heart then pumps the oxygenated blood around the body. Pretty damn unique and remarkable!

- **Depending on the species, adults can range from less than 0.5mm long (the *Chaetogaster annandalei*) to the giant Gippsland of Australia, which averages 1m in length.**
  One giant Gippsland was recorded at just over 2m! That's taller than Darth Vader – making it a big ol' worm and a potential new lead for *Star Wars*...

Animal magnetism, earthworm-style

Inspiring zoologist, writer and broadcaster Megan McCubbin enlightened us on the subject of earthworm courtship and reproduction, when she joined us on the show. Finding out about earthworm sex was a real eye-opener. I hope I do it justice...

Earthworms are solitary animals. They all have individual burrows in the soil. When they're a few months to a year old, potential partners will meet up in a burrow. They do this at least 12 times. Earthworms essentially go on a series of dates to get to know one another before they copulate. It's all very *Pride and Prejudice*...

```
                    CUT TO:
    The exquisite drawing room of an 18th-
century earthworm's burrow. Jane Earthworm
    Bennet is sitting playing a harp. Mr
     Earthworm Darcy enters the room.


         Mr Earthworm Darcy:
       Good morning, Miss Bennet.
    Is your sister Elizabeth here today?


        Jane Earthworm Bennet:
    I'm sorry Mr Darcy. Dear Elizabeth is
       out decomposing the garden.
```

Once two earthworms have been on a number of dates (and consent from both sets of parents has been obtained) they position their bodies parallel to one another.

Now let's press pause for a moment. Before we – or indeed the earthworms – go any further, let me mention that earthworms are hermaphrodites. This means every one of them has both male and female sexual organs. OK, back to our two earthworms...

So, the two earthworms – who are hermaphrodites, remember – are parallel. Their bodies are aligned with one another (but with their bodies facing opposite directions, head to tail). Each earthworm now positions both its sexual organs – the penis and vagina – with the other earthworm's opposite organs (similar to the positive and minus of an AA battery). The two amorous earthworms are aligned and put their opposite sex organs next to one another.

As they start canoodling, both earthworms excrete a load of mucus. As you do.

In fact, the two earthworms excrete so much mucus that a mucus bubble forms around their bodies. Each worm then ejaculates sperm into this mucus bubble and the sperm is deposited into the other worm's sperm receptacle. The earthworm mating is now complete; they both lie back, light a cigarette and read out some Baudelaire. No they don't, earthworms are into E.E. Cummings. Anyway... with copulation accomplished, the two earthworms now go their separate ways. But the reproduction process continues...

BONUS SEXY EARTHWORM FACT:

Did you know that mating between earthworms can last up to 200 minutes? Although 198 minutes of that is spent working out which end is which.

Taking it to the next level, earthworm-style...

Let's return to the two earthworms. They had started going their separate ways, post copulation...

When you look at an earthworm you'll often see a thickened bit behind the head. This is called the clitella. And before you ask, no... the clitella isn't a clitoris made of Nutella.

Our two earthworms have moved apart but now, out of their clitellas, each produces a new mucus bubble. This bubble slips forward towards the mouth end of one worm. As the bubble moves forward, across the worm's body, the mucus passes over the worm's own sacks of eggs. These egg sacks stick to the mucal slime. Then, as the mucus bubble continues moving up, it passes over the other worm's sperm (which, if you remember, are in the sperm receptacle). The eggs and sperm come into contact in this new bubble and, if all goes to plan, the eggs are fertilised. I understand now why my pitch to remake *Eyes Wide Shut* with earthworms didn't gain any traction.

The slimy mucus bubble containing the fertilised eggs is then wriggled off the earthworm's head. This bubble forms a cocoon for the fertilised eggs (normally between four and 20 eggs). The worm then buries the cocoon of eggs into the soil. About three weeks later, the new-born worms hatch and leave the cocoon. Hurray! Brand new baby earthworms!

Amazingly, adult earthworms can repeat this reproduction process every seven to ten days; which is why earthworm populations tend to grow so quickly.

If all this earthworm sex chat has got you hot under the collar, here's a top not-sexy earthworm fact, to help cool things down...

BONUS NOT-SEXY EARTHWORM FACT:

Did you know that many earthworms can regrow parts of their bodies if severed? For example, most worms can regrow their tails if severed.

Even more incredible, scientists at Harvard University have found that if you take a 'three-banded panther worm' and chop it in thirds, each section regenerates independently. This means that within eight days you'll have three healthy new worms, all with their own mouth, brain and tail! Three worms for the price of one! Isn't nature a wonderful thing (and full of bargains if you know where to look).

But when it comes to body regeneration, worms aren't alone in the animal kingdom. Let's find out who else can regrow lost body parts by playing a quick round of that Saturday teatime favourite – **The Regeneration Game!**

In keeping with the classic gameshow format, we've put a load of animals on a conveyer belt (none of them were hurt during the writing of this game, but several have been fictitiously Blu-Tacked to stop them falling off). As each animal passes by, I'm going to tell you a fascinating fact about it regenerating and you have to decide whether it's true or false.

1. **First on the conveyor belt – it's a spider. Spiders can regrow lost legs and even bits of legs. Do you think that's true or false?**

ANSWER: **It's true:** Spiders can regrow missing legs when they moult. Which only leaves the question – why have Marvel chickened out of doing that with Tom Holland?

2. **Next in line... how about the leech? Leeches can regrow any segment of their body that happens to get lopped off. True or false?**

ANSWER: **That's false:** Although the leech is a kind of worm, it can't regrow segments like the earthworm does. Sucker.

3. **Oh look, it's a cuddly starfish! True or false – not only can some starfish regrow their arms, but a whole new starfish can grow from one of those lopped-off arms.**

ANSWER: **It's true:** Imagine being the starfish that lost the original arm and bumping into the new one. 'Hey, you look familiar...'

> 4.   Who's this on the conveyor belt? It's an axolotl! The axolotl is an amphibious form of salamander and is able to regrow parts of its jaw. True or false?
>
> ANSWER: **It's true!** Axolotls are amazing at regenerating body parts: they can perfectly regrow limbs and tails as well as parts of their heart, brain and lower jaw. Basically, everything the typical cabinet minister lacks.

And that whistle I've just made up means it's the end of **The Regeneration Game**. Well done everybody!

Before we check in on our next member of the animal magnetism group, let me give you one final earthworm fact. I think it's a humdinger…

BONUS EARTHWORM FACT:

Did you know that some earthworms eject fluid out of their backs when they're stressed? The fluid, coelomic fluid, remoistens the body to help the earthworm get away.

The blue squirter earthworm can project the fluid up to 30cm. Which is impressive, until it's the fourth office party in a row at which he's done it and everyone's like, 'Alright Tony, get another trick mate.'

So that's our look at earthworms. What a fascinating, bizarre romantic life they lead. I hope you now appreciate earthworms in a whole new – if a bit mucus-y – light!

Time now for our next example of animal magnetism. Be careful, because this animal can be a bit spiky when it comes to matters of the heart...

Porcupine

Give it up for the porcupine: the prickliest of rodents and a most striking animal.

Porcupines are large, round rodents covered in long pointy quills. Most porcupines are approximately 60–90cm long, with a tail that's around 30cm long. Imagine a massive hedgehog with longer, more pronounced sharp spikes and you're kind of there.

There are 30 different species of porcupine spread across the world – from tropical Asia to southern Europe, and from Africa to North and South America. In terms of their habitat, North and South American porcupines live in trees, whilst African porcupines live in rocky environments.

BONUS PORCUPINE FACT:

Porcupines hold the record for being the longest-living rodent. A porcupine called Cooper (great name for a porcupine) was the animal ambassador at the Museum of Science in Boston. Cooper lived for a staggering 33 years, before he sadly passed away in 2021.

The secret to Cooper's long life? A diet of grated carrot and sweet potato cake, with smashed banana icing and corn kernel sprinkles on top. I could have me a plate of that!

Porcupines and their prickly coats…

You definitely know when you've seen a porcupine: their coats are covered in long, sharp spiky quills. These quills are modified hairs, coated with thick keratin to give them rigidity and strength. All in, porcupines have about 30,000 quills. Smaller porcupines (the ones in the Americas) have quills that are around 10cm long. Larger African porcupines have quills that are 50cm long.

Their sizeable quills protect porcupines against predators. On a basic level, the quills are a visual warning for other animals not to mess. But more than this, porcupines can make their quills erect when they feel threatened. This results in the porcupine looking two or three times bigger than it really is, which helps to ward off predators. But if the erect quills don't deter a predator, porcupines can also charge backwards and prickle an enemy. This sounds eccentric, but it's most effective. Fair to say the predator doesn't see it coming!

There have also been studies into the antibiotic properties of porcupine quills. The quills are coated in free fatty acids, and it's believed that these acids may provide first-aid for a porcupine that has suffered a self-injury (an occupational hazard for any porcupine looking for love!).

Procreating porcupines…

With bodies covered in 30,000 sharp quills, how do a male and female porcupine get close enough to mate? We were fortunate that esteemed zoologist, writer and broadcaster Lucy Cooke shared the porcupines' secret on the show…

Lucy informed us that there's a lot of screaming when porcupines have sex, but the screaming begins before the male and female have even got close. Porcupine courtship starts when a female screams out loud; she's letting the nearby males know that she's fertile and ready. Upon hearing the female's big scream, a gang of prospective males soon turn up. The males proceed to do what males of all species are good at: they have a scrap. To the victor, the dubious – potentially life-threatening – right to seduce the sharp-prickled female.

How do porcupines mate without prickling each other?

The Christmas cracker answer is: carefully. The real answer is surprising and, dare I say it, funnier…

Once a male porcupine has won the right to mate, he approaches the female boldly, displaying his erect penis. The male then proceeds to spray a high-pressure jet of his own urine onto the female. He delivers this golden shower of love for two reasons: to impress the female AND to get her in the mood (a somewhat unorthodox but fruitful technique).

It transpires that a male porcupine's urine contains hormones that make females receptive. Female porcupines are fertile for only eight hours a year, so the male doesn't have time to waste; he has to pull out the big guns and fast.

Once she's been sprayed with urine, if the female porcupine isn't interested, she'll growl, and the male knows to back off. But if the female is game, she'll raise her quills and tail, presenting her backside to the male. By moving her quills forward, she's making sure the male won't get punctured. When it comes to porcupine sex, always remember: safety first!

At this point the male lifts his front paws and walks on his hind legs towards the female, until her raised tail touches and supports his tummy. The female's tail supports the male and stops him from fatally puncturing himself on her quills.

The male stays on his hind legs, whilst his forelegs hold the female's tail for balance. This means the male isn't putting any weight on the female during sex. In fact, the male doesn't need to get physically close to the female during sex, thanks to – you guessed it – its relatively long penis.

So, that's the remarkable tale of how porcupines get up close and personal. A story filled with danger, intrigue and jets of urine.

BONUS NOT RAUNCHY PORCUPINE FACT:

Did you know that a baby porcupine is called a porcupette? When born, a porcupette's quills are soft hair. Clearly it would be a fate worse than death (or at least as bad as death) for a female to give birth to a spiky child! Within a few days the porcupette's hairs harden and eventually form sharp adult quills.

Let me finish our look at these bizarre, brave lovers with a piece of advice for you. The next time you put this book down, if you're in need of a giggle and a bit of joy, I highly recommend you go on the internet and search for porcupine sounds. You see, porcupines sound exactly like Morph, the classic, much-loved clay animation character. Hearing porcupine calls always brings a smile to my face and makes me giggle.

Our final animal in this lustful group demonstrates a highly original approach to courtship and reproduction. You might argue this next creature is a strong contender for unlucky in love rather than animal magnetism. Whatever your take, there's an extraordinary tragic love story for you here...

Australian Redback Spider

Over the course of making many episodes of *Nature Table*, we've learned that spiders can fly (what on earth?) and grow to be 30cm wide (yikes). It's now time to add to this hair-raising list by focusing on the sex lives of spiders. Well, the sex life of one spider in particular...

A highly venomous spider, the Australian redback spider is found in Australia, New Zealand and Southeast Asia. Females have a round black body with a distinctive red stripe on the top side of the abdomen and an orangey red hourglass mark under the abdomen. Females are typically 10mm long, whilst males are a diminutive 4mm long.

Usually active at night, redback spiders prey on insects and other spiders that get caught in their webs. Redbacks kill by biting their prey and injecting venom via its two fangs (think Dracula). After biting its prey, the spider wraps it in silk and sucks out the victim's liquefied insides. Gruesome but effective!

Based on their uncompromising eating habits, it should come as little surprise that – when it comes to romance – redback spiders are on the more aggressive end of the spectrum. Bunches of roses need not apply…

What makes redback spiders stand out when it comes to reproduction?

As leading entomologist Dr Karim Vahed informed us on the show, two sweet words can sum up the unusual mating habits of Redback spiders: 'sexual' and 'cannibalism'.

Research has shown that sexual cannibalism in Australian redbacks is widespread: in 60 to 80 per cent of cases, during copulation, the female will eat the male.

As Karim explained, scientists first thought this cannibalism was the female taking advantage of the male; getting herself a free meal. However, we now know that the male is wilfully complicit in being eaten. During copulation, male redbacks actively somersault their bodies towards the female, so she can start eating them during copulation. It's incredible and strange. Why are you doing it guys?!

In about two thirds of cases, females fully consume the male whilst mating continues. It's great that the male willingly volunteers to make dinner – even if dinner happens to be his bottom on a plate.

But why do male redbacks offer themselves to the female in this kamikaze way? Again, Karim was good enough to spill the beans. He referenced a set of studies that said male redbacks can copulate for longer, and therefore transfer more sperm to the female, if they're eaten. In one study, males who were eaten by the female during sex copulated for twice as long than those who didn't! You can see the TV infomercial now…

Hey guys!
We've got a new way for you to last
longer in the bedroom!
There's just one small downside…

There is another potential bonus for a male being eaten during copulation. Yippee for being eaten! You see, females who have eaten a male are more likely to reject subsequent males. This means that more of the dead male's genetic material is passed on. (As Karim confirmed, it's surprising that no male spiders have ever taken a vow of chastity.)

BONUS SEXY SPIDER FACT:

It's heartening to know that some male spider species actively avoid being cannibalised. Rather than be submissive, one male spider species – *Thanatus fabricii* – bites and ties up the female with strands of silk before mating, so that the female cannot cannibalise him.

All I'm saying is it's a matter of time before somebody pitches a new film: *Fifty Shades of Spider.*

I know what you're thinking at this point. This look at spider sex is all very fascinating and weird. Whilst we're on the subject, can you tell us...

How do spiders actually mate?

Thank you for asking... I'll gladly answer your question.

Karim explained that male spiders don't transfer sperm with their penis. They do things differently. Instead of a penis, spiders use their front limbs: specifically, a pair of limbs around the mouth called pedipalps. Each pedipalp has a syringe on it. So, effectively, spiders have two penises. Of course they do...

The male 'charges up' these two pedipalp syringes with his sperm. He does this by squirting a fluid that contains his sperm – from his gonads – onto a tiny 'sperm web'. He then sucks the sperm directly into his pedipalps (his two penises) and stores the sperm until it's time for mating. This is a process known as 'sperm induction' and it can take from a few minutes to a few hours to complete (I assume depending on how well-endowed the spider is).

When it comes to the act of copulation, male spiders have their two penises and females have two vaginas. As research has shown – by being eaten – not only can a male spider prolong the insertion of his pedipalps, but he also has a greater chance of inserting not one but both his pedipalps; hence double the chance of reproductive success. Oh, the bittersweet tears...

'Love is when you meet someone and eat them.'
Famous redback spider and poet, Judith Wobbles

So, you now know that female redback spiders often eat their mates. But they're not always this greedy. Redbacks can in fact survive without food for a whopping 100 days. But which animals can go even longer without food? Let's find out with a round of the biggest gameshow on Spanish TV – **The Other Hunger Games.**

Here's how it works: I'll name an animal and you have to tell me if you think it can go for longer or shorter periods without food than the preceding animal.

Let's begin. We now know the redback spider can go 100 days without resorting to Deliveroo.

1.   **But what about the scorpion? Can it last a longer or shorter time without needing to eat?**

ANSWER: **It's longer.** The scorpion can go up to a year without eating. To maintain such a slow metabolism, scorpions can spend over 90 per cent of their lives inactive. Which is the opposite of me; the longer I sit in front of Netflix the more I eat, but they're both valid evolutionary strategies.

2. **OK – here's another one. What about the great white shark? Can this shark go without for a longer or shorter period than the scorpion?**

ANSWER: **It's way shorter**. The great white shark can go three months without eating. But their morning coffee is non-negotiable.

3. **How about the Galapagos tortoise? Do you think this gentle giant can go for a longer or shorter time than three months without eating?**

ANSWER: **It's longer.** The Galapagos tortoise can go without eating or drinking for up to a year, storing food and water to survive the long Galapagos dry season. To put that in context, the Very Hungry Caterpillar can't even wait for you to turn the page. It just eats straight through.

4.   **Here's another for you – the alligator. Can an alligator last for longer or less than a year without food?**

ANSWER: **It's longer**. The alligator can actually wait two to three years between meals! Thanks to fat stores in its tail and its slow, cold-blooded metabolism. I once went two and a half years between courses at a wedding. At least it felt like that.

And finally, last one…

5.   **The tardigrade, or water bear, which is a microscopic water-dwelling organism. (Check them out online: tardigrades look just like a Dr Who character.) Do you think the tardigrade can go longer or shorter than three years between meals?**

ANSWER: **It's much longer**. The tardigrade can go without feeding for 30 years. Imagine the jubilation of the scientists who finally got this conclusion after watching one do nothing for 30 years.

And that's the end of the game – mainly because it's been minutes since my last meal. Baba ghanoush, anyone?

And on that note, this is me calling a close to our look at animal magnetism in the animal kingdom. If I'm honest, I think this group may benefit from a different title: *Fatal Attraction* springs to mind. Or maybe *Basic Insect* (hangs head in shame and gets coat...)

BITESIZE NATURE TABLE

Before we move on to our next *Nature Table* group of animals, here are some travel-size *Nature Table* facts for you – ideal for when you urgently need some quick flora and fauna facts for that long journey ahead.

Did you know...?

Hummingbirds use so much energy flying that they eat up to eight times their body weight a day. Which is exactly the same reason I do it too. Apart from the energy bit. And the flying.

Though everyone knows tomatoes are technically a fruit, they're legally defined as vegetables in the USA. Useful information if you ever want to sue a tomato.

Owls can turn their heads an amazing 270 degrees. Humans can manage up to 160, unless they work in panto, where we have to do the work for them.

The leaves of the monk's pepper plant used to be placed into undergarments 'to cool the heat of lust'. The idea was that you're not going to fancy anyone with a load of shrubbery in their pants.

BESIDE THE SEASIDE

I love being by the sea. Standing on a beach, looking out at the endless blue (sometimes brown – thanks, water companies) and decluttering my brain of all the silly nonsense that lands in there.

All the creatures in our next group can be seen around different areas of the UK coastline. If you happen to be near the coast and go for a walk or a boat trip, you could be lucky enough to make their acquaintance.

So, let's grab our virtual binoculars, put on our imaginary wellies, zip up our fictitious raincoats (better safe than sorry) and have a proper look at what's happening beside the seaside.

Picture yourself sitting on a seaside promenade. You're looking out at the deep blue sea. It's a beautiful sunny day. There's no breeze. The sea is still. The sun is shimmering on the waves. Everything is beautiful. All is calm. But calm soon turns to bedlam as you hear the distinctive loud squawks of our first seaside creature…

Herring Gull

Welcome to Britain's most misunderstood bird… the European herring gull. Herring gulls get a bad rap from us. This is mainly because they're noisy, they do splatted poos the size of omelettes, and sometimes swoop down to steal our chips. This is us humans doing what we do so well: deciding an animal's worth based on how it might affect us. We really are self-important prats.

Before I make the case for why herring gulls are in fact phenomenal, here are some introductory gull facts for you…

FACT 1: Found in the coastal areas of western Europe, herring gulls are the most abundant of all gull species worldwide.

FACT 2: Herring gulls are large birds. They can average between 55cm (females) and 65cm (males) in length. In terms of their markings, adults have a white head and undercarriage, with light grey wings and yellow bills.

FACT 3: The first 'gulls' appeared around the same time as humans, 200,000 to 300,000 years ago, which is interesting because the seagull was actually nature's third attempt at creating this bird. The A-gull and B-gull weren't quite right. Come on! That's almost a funny joke! Give me a break.

FACT 4: Herring gulls can have long lives. The greatest recorded age is a whopping 49 years!

FACT 5: We tend to refer to all gulls as 'seagulls', but this is a misnomer. 'Seagull' is the name of a large group of seabirds, but isn't a species. Around the British Isles there are 25 different species of 'gull'; all with different names, such as the common gull and black-headed gull. Our focus today is on the herring gull. Herring gulls are the ones we often see by the seaside.

Herring gulls are chancers trying to steal my chips! What's so good about them?

When top conservationist Dr Holly Smith-Baedorf joined us on the show, we were lucky that she really opened our eyes to herring gulls. There's so much more to them than the prejudices we project onto them. Let's look at what Holly shared...

- **Herring gulls are super-intelligent**
  Gulls make great parents (more on this later) and despite us draining their natural food sources, herring gulls are amazing survivors. Their continued survival is down to their seriously impressive brains and remarkable evolution.

- **Herring gulls use bread as bait to lure a fish**
  Using a piece of bread as bait is an example of tool use in the animal kingdom. Tool use is very rare in non-humans and a sign of great intelligence in herring gulls. Go you brainiac gulls!

- **Herring gulls are 'worm charmers'**
  Herring gulls are fiendish when it comes to catching
  worms. They know that worms rise to the surface when
  soil is damp, so herring gulls do an elaborate tap dance on
  grass (known as 'worm charming'). The vibrations from
  their tap-dancing feet mimics rain hitting the soil, which
  in turn 'charms' worms to the surface. I highly recommend
  you check out gulls 'worm charming' online; it's a brilliant,
  joyous sight.

- **Herring gulls have an incredible evolutionary
  adaptation when it comes to staying hydrated**
  Herring gulls drink freshwater when they can, but they
  also drink salty seawater when there's no other option.
  To do this, they have glands above their eyes to filter
  and excrete the salt in the water. You can see the salty
  excretion come out of the herring gull's nostrils. Other
  seabirds also have this adaptation. And sea turtles have a
  similar adaptation: they stay hydrated by crying salty tears!
  So, if you see a sea turtle crying, don't be sad – they're
  just hydrating themselves (unless, of course, they've just
  watched the Hollywood classic *Casablanca*).

Herring gulls are surprisingly sociable, showing empathy

As impressive as it is, there's more to herring gulls than tap dancing
for their dinner. As Holly explained, what really should have you
thinking twice about gulls is their remarkable scope for empathy...

Herring gulls live in groups. They're sociable animals who look out for each other. As an example, when a herring gull finds enough food to share, it'll call loudly to the rest of the group. This behaviour is way more hospitable than I am when my partner tries to snaffle my French fries in a restaurant. 'If you want chips, order your own chips!'

Herring gulls' scope for empathy even extends to other gulls' chicks. Herring gulls often raise their chicks on roofs, because high-up roofs give good protection from predators. If a baby chick accidentally strays too far and falls off a roof (which does happen) then it's not just the parents that swoop to the rescue; the whole group will rescue and protect each other's young against predators. So, you could argue, herring gulls have mastered the combined arts of Neighbourhood Watch and decent childcare facilities.

And whilst we're talking herring gull chicks, here's a fun fact...

Herring gull chicks make a plaintive high-pitched squeak. The chicks do this whining call to adults as a way of saying, 'Give me food.' Amazingly, gull chicks can do this 'squeak' call whilst still inside the egg; and adult gulls will do this call back to them. Good parenting skills, right?

Even more remarkable and/or sickening is the fact that adult gulls will take this form of 'baby talk' and do it to one another during courtship. Yes, you read that right: herring gulls baby talk to each other to be romantic. I assume it translates as, 'Come here often? Fancy a chip?'

★ **SUPER BONUS HERRING GULL ROMANCE FACTS:**

Did you know that herring gulls are monogamous and pair up for life?

When a male herring gull is interested in a female, he'll regurgitate some food for her. The old 'impress a mate by regurgitating' technique: a ploy used in kebab shops all over the UK on Friday and Saturday nights.

This is all great, but there's still too many of them....

European herring gull numbers have decreased by a ginormous 60 per cent in the last 25 years. Today, they're on the RSPB's 'Red List' of endangered species, the highest possible conservation status.

Many scientists believe this dramatic decrease in the population is down to our collective actions: we build on gulls' nesting sites and fish unsustainably, making it harder for gulls to survive. Because of our actions, we've forced these birds to become scavengers. By starving gulls out, we've created the monster we perceive. That's on us, not the gulls.

Most gulls are shy

We think that gulls are bold as brass and opportunistic. But it's only a small minority of gulls that are confident enough to come close and try to steal our chips.

Researchers at the University of Exeter have studied gull behaviour and discovered that a majority of gulls are nervous and shy around humans.

The fact is most gulls prefer to stay away from us. To a gull, we're like a big scary Godzilla (especially when we're wearing a big scary Godzilla costume).

And on the subject of gulls grabbing our food, here's some advice...

TOP TIPS FOR NOT GETTING YOUR CHIPS STOLEN BY GULLS:

- **Stand with your back to a wall as you eat your chips.** Unsurprisingly, gulls aren't fans of dive-bombing a wall.

- **Keep food hidden and secure.** Gulls are so clever they've been known to go through bags on the beach if you go for a swim!

- **Eat green food.** Or dye your fish and chips green! It sounds eccentric but research has proven that gulls – like children – are less likely to steal green foods. Gulls have more powerful colour vision than humans and it may be they prefer food that they observe us regularly

> eating. If the food is presented in an unusual colour,
> then the herring gull is initially unsure and steers clear
> of it. Time to start ordering peas!

Herring gulls are magnificent, highly intelligent survivalists. And as I mentioned earlier, they make good, attentive parents – using baby talk with their young. But not every species is quite so nurturing. So, which animals were brought up by great parents and which weren't so lucky? Let's find out in a quick game of the worldwide TV ratings smash, **I Blame the Parents**.

In this game I'll name an animal and you're going to tell me if you think it's a good parent, or a rubbish one. If you've ever wondered why so many sea bass are in therapy, then this quiz is for you.

1.   **Let's start with orangutans. How are they as mothers? Are they more likely to get a box of chocolates at Christmas or a visit from social services?**

ANSWER: **Orangutans are great mums**. They have a strong bond with their young, who completely rely on them for the first two years and stay with them for up to seven... Or until the mother drops enough hints. 'Oh look darling, here's the website of a charity that adopts us!'

2. **Next, burying beetles. What are they burying: small vertebrate carcasses or their paternal responsibilities?**

ANSWER: **Burying beetles are bad dads.** The male mates with a female and initially sticks around to help care for the larvae. BUT all the time he'll be trying to attract other females, abandoning the nest before the larvae hatch. Some beetles roll up balls of poo and eat them, but abandoning your beetle babies? That really stinks.

3. **How about harp seal mothers? Do they give nice blubbery hugs or are they cold as ice?**

ANSWER: **Harp seals are terrible mums.** Harp seals are only attentive parents for around 12 days. After that, they abandon their pups to go off mating again. The pups are left stranded on the ice, where they lose half their body weight and are at constant risk of getting eaten.

Surely this is the real psychopath test: could you look a baby seal in the face and still pack your suitcase?

4.   **And finally... the hardhead catfish. Is this hardhead a hardarse when it comes to being a good dad?**

ANSWER: **The hardhead catfish is a great dad!** As the old saying goes, 'hard head, soft heart'. Move aside seahorses: the hardhead catfish dad carries up to 48 eggs in his mouth until they hatch. How does he avoid swallowing them? He starves for two months until the baby fish hatch and swim away.

That's basically having a mouthful of caviar for two months and not swallowing it. Which is really impressive – I can't even be in the same room as a KitKat.

Sadly, that's the end of this game of **I Blame The Parents**. Before we move on, I did earlier promise to tell you why so many bass fish are in therapy. Bass fathers have been known to eat their young after they're born. You see, even sea bass think sea bass are delicious.

Anyway, let's say goodbye to the wonderful herring gulls and let them practise their tap dancing.

Time for us now to say hello – or indeed *olá* – to our next member of the beside the seaside club...

Portuguese Man o'War

The Portuguese man o'war. It's an intriguing name that leaves you wanting to know more... like Welsh rarebit or Cumberland ring. I reckon most of you have heard the name – Portugese man o'war – but you're not certain what it actually is. Fear not, as you're about to find out lots about this brilliantly unique and mysterious sea creature...

Drifting along in the sea, often washing up on beaches, the Portuguese man o'war looks like a jellyfish. I say 'looks like' because it's not actually a jellyfish. More on that soon.

The Portuguese man o'war has a balloon-like transparent bladder, called a pneumatophore. Filled with gas, this bladder can be bright blue, violet or pink in colour (or sometimes all three in the sun). In terms of its shape, the bladder looks very much like a see-through Cornish pasty – it even has the crimping! – and can be between 9 and 30cm long. The inflated bladder enables the man o'war to float and drift on the surface of the sea.

Deadly tentacles!

Attached to the gas-filled pasty-shaped bladder are a number of long, thin, venomous tentacles. These long tentacles trail underwater and are typically 10m long (at least that's what they claim on their Tinder profile). The tentacles are powerful enough to kill fish and do some serious damage to humans (though they're rarely fateful for humans).

> ## BONUS PORTUGUESE MAN O'WAR FACT:
>
> Where does the name 'Portuguese man o'war' come from?
> The story behind the name is that this intriguing sea creature resembles a 15th-century Portuguese sailing warship. Sitting above the water, the man o'war's large inflated bladder resembles one of these historical wooden ships at full sail.

Man o'wars live at the surface of the ocean; the Atlantic and Indian Oceans are its common habitats. With its bladder keeping it buoyant and acting as a sail, Portuguese man o'wars have been known to drift 1,000 miles! They tend to drift in groups and can wash up on beaches.

I remember when we featured Portuguese man o'wars on the show, ace zoologist and broadcaster Billy Heaney was going to talk about them. But Billy wasn't sure he'd be able to source one to bring to the studio. Thankfully, the week before the recording, there was a big storm in Cornwall and a few man o'wars washed up on our local beach. My brave/foolhardy partner went out with a plastic takeaway box and a stick and managed to put a dead one into a clean sealed box that had contained a Thai green curry the night before. We put it in the fridge, I drove it up to London the next day and the show had its specimen. That's sciencey showbiz!

NB. It's worth noting that when they're beached, Portuguese man o'wars can still sting. So never pick one up out of curiosity!

BONUS MAN O'WAR SHOWBIZ ANECDOTE:

When we talked about man o'wars on the show, our marvellous host Sue Perkins recalled being abroad on holiday and getting stung by one. Not only did Sue remember it being super-painful, but she was also surprised by how many people on the beach suddenly wanted to wee on her! Sue quickly discovered this was to ease the pain (it wasn't a kinky beach thing)!

I should point out that there's no scientific evidence that weeing on a jellyfish or man o'war sting eases the pain. At best it's an urban myth, perhaps perpetuated by people who like weeing on people! I'll leave that thought with you.

Standing out from the crowd

Portuguese man o'wars are striking to look at and they're poisonous. But what makes them so unique and special?

As I mentioned earlier, a Portuguese man o'war looks like a jellyfish. But it isn't. As Billy Heaney explained on the show, man o'wars aren't jellyfish... they're siphonophores (which are very complex organisms). They appear to be a single creature, but in fact Portuguese man o'wars are known as 'a colonial organism'.

What then is a colonial organism? Another – perhaps simpler – way of describing a man o'war would be as a 'collection of animals'. A man o'war looks like one single creature, but actually it's several creatures, all joined together. There are four specific sections (or zooids) to a man o'war. Each section has a specific task for the colony as a whole. These four tasks include floating, reproduction, catching prey and feeding.

So, what we have are several independent organisms that are fused to look like a single creature. These organisms are working together as one. They all have different jobs. And they all need one another to survive as a group.

Teamwork in action

A clear example of the organisms working together as one can be seen when man o'wars hunt and eat their prey...

For a Portuguese man o'war, hunting begins with its long tentacles dangling in the sea. Each tentacle has thousands of stinging cells. A stray fish who gets too close to a tentacle is stung and paralysed. Immediately the powerful tentacle starts reeling in the startled fish, moving the fish to the man o'war's digestive polyps. At this point – with the help of powerful chemicals – the fish is liquified and digested. As deaths go, I reckon 'liquified' is as harsh as it gets, but you can't deny that what the man o'war does is impressive. It's quite the team effort for this colony of organisms, working together for a common – if gruesome – purpose.

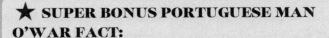

★ SUPER BONUS PORTUGUESE MAN O'WAR FACT:

Portuguese man o'wars have such insatiable appetites that they can sting and eat 100 small fish a day.

I think 100 fish a day is really good going. I'll be honest, I can see a new daytime TV show in the offing: *Portuguese Man o'War vs Food*. Every episode, we see if a regular Portuguese man o'war – sitting in a trattoria – can liquify and put away 800 plates of spaghetti. With all those tentacles it must have a chance. Obviously the man o'war would be wearing a bib. Tell me you wouldn't watch that?

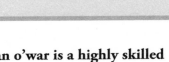

The Portuguese man o'war is a highly skilled predator, but…

Man o'wars may be expert hunters, but as is so often the case in the natural world, the tables can be turned. Loggerhead turtles, ocean sunfish and blanket octopus all eat Portuguese man o'wars. In fact, the large blanket octopus (so named because of the webbing between their tentacles) has been spotted with man o'war tendrils attached to its suckers. It could be that the blanket octopus is wearing the man o'war's tendrils to help it catch prey and defend against predators. The blanket octopus gets itself a free meal *and* a handy surprise weapon – two for the price of none! Also an excellent example of upcycling in the natural world.

That said, if a man o'war meets a threat on the ocean's surface, it can deflate its gas-filled bladder, to sink below the water. So, so clever!

So, that's our look at this brightly coloured see-through Cornish pasty lookalike, the Portuguese man o'war. With its crimped mohawk-like feature on the top, this is a properly punk sea predator. Looking like a single creature, but actually being four organisms working as a team, this keen predator is a perfect example of nature's properly genius engineering. With no means of propulsion and drifting across oceans, often ending up beside the seaside, the Portuguese man o'war is one tough colonial organism.

It's time now for us to put the kettle on (mine's a black coffee please) and welcome another mysterious creature of the deep blue sea...

This fish we're checking out can be seen in the southern and western coastal seas of the UK. I've been lucky enough to see one a couple of times: once on a boat trip from St Ives and then on a boat off Porthgwarra, close to Land's End. So, if you're lucky and have a keen eye, this extraordinary outlandish exotic fish is one you could potentially see beside the seaside...

Ocean Sunfish

Native to temperate and tropical waters around the world, ocean sunfish are spotted in the seas off the UK in the warmer summer months. They come to our coast to feed on jellyfish.

The ocean sunfish is one of the largest bony fish in the world. They can weigh up to a tonne, and grow up to a humungous 4.5m long and 4m high (for reference 4m is roughly the length of two king-size mattresses lined up end to end).

NB. When I went online and typed in '4 metres for context', one website told me that 4 metres is equivalent to a T-rex's hips. Thank you, internet, for clarifying! What would I do without you?

So, ocean sunfish are BIG. But what do they actually look like?

I'm going to try my best – with words – to describe the look of an ocean sunfish. They're seriously peculiar looking, so I recommend you look them up online. I guarantee that whatever I say won't do this highly unusual fish justice!

Ocean sunfish are massive, flat and circular. I'd say they look like a giant swimming round flat head. Or, to paint a picture, imagine an enormous pancake, with an elongated dorsal fin on the neck (or top) and an anal fin underneath. They kind of look like that.

What's interesting is that ocean sunfish don't have tails. Instead, they have a rigid fringe of skin that enables them to steer themselves: acting like a ship's rudder.

BONUS OCEAN SUNFISH FACT:

The ancient Latin word for ocean sunfish is *mola mola*. This translates as 'millstone' and alludes to the fish's grey, round body and rough texture.

In German a sunfish is called a *schwimmender Kopf*. This literally translates as 'swimming head'. I think this is a fair and precise – if lacking in whimsy – description of what an ocean sunfish looks like. They're wonderful but weird!

So, why do we call them 'sunfish'?

If you're in a boat, you'll often spot an ocean sunfish basking on its side; with the long dorsal fin flapping on the surface. Essentially, they're sunbathing!

One theory for this basking in the sun, is that it's raising the fish's body temperature after feeding in deep cooler waters (they can dive up to 790m!) Ocean sunfish love the warmth of the sun.

Another theory for why sunfish bask on the sea's surface and have their name is because they want to dislodge the parasites from their body. By lying flat on the surface, basking in the sun, birds can stand directly on them and peck off the parasites. This may sound a bit far-fetched, but a Japanese research vessel in the North Pacific witnessed this happen…

You see, sunfish carry parasites called *Penella*. These parasites bury themselves into the sunfish's flesh and leave a trail of eggs hanging out. A group of Japanese scientists noticed that a school of sunfish were following a rookery (group) of albatrosses. The fish were trying to attract the birds, by exposing their sides to them.

The albatrosses started diving down and getting their parasite snack. An incredible and rare example of a cross-species symbiotic relationship between fish and birds. Whoop! Whoop!

 SUPER BONUS OCEAN SUNFISH FACT:

Bit of ocean sunfish folklore for you here... Polynesians are known to have called the sunfish 'King of Mackerel'. It was considered bad luck to kill sunfish, for fear that their loss could prevent mackerel from finding their way to Polynesia's group of islands.

Whole lotta sunfish eggs

Not only are ocean sunfish big when it comes to their physical size (two lined-up king-size mattresses, if you remember), but they also produce more eggs than any living vertebrate. That's right: ocean sunfish are egg-laying record-breakers!

How many eggs do you think an ocean sunfish produces?

Is it 1? No. Higher!

100? No. Higher!

1,000? No. Higher!

1 million? No. Higher!

10 million? No.

9.9999996 million? No, I'm not being sneaky. Go higher!

100 million? No.

I'll give you the answer now, before the next seven pages of this book are hijacked into being 'Guess the large number!'…
   Ocean sunfish produce 300 million eggs!!!!! 300 million eggs is a mind-blowing number of eggs. I looked it up online and – for context – 300 million eggs is the equivalent of 300 million eggs. In technical terms, this amount of eggs is 'a lot'.

So, why do sunfish lay so many eggs?

We believe it's because ocean sunfish are such solitary fish; it's not easy for them to find a mate. So, they make the most of their chance encounters with a member of the opposite sex and produce 'a lot' of eggs.
   It's funny, but all this egg talk has given me an idea for a game…
   As you now know, the female sunfish produces 300 million eggs. But how do other animals compare? Let's find out with a round of everyone's favourite egg-comparison game **Play Your Clutch Right**. A clutch is of course the amount of eggs produced by an animal at one time. But you all knew that… I believe in you.

I'm going to now give you a list of animals and you have to tell me if the number of eggs they lay is higher or lower than the previous one – starting with our old friend the sunfish, who can lay up to 300 million eggs at one time.

1. **So, to start us off... how about the grey partridge? Do they produce a higher or lower number of eggs than the sunfish?**

ANSWER: **It's much lower** – a sunfish lays up to 300 million eggs at a time, while the grey partridge lays around 22. That does however make it the bird that lays the most eggs at once. So, any grey partridges reading this, please don't feel too inadequate.

2. **Next up is a seahorse. More or less eggs than the grey partridge's 22? And I know it should be 'more or fewer' but who says that? Nerds, that's who.**

ANSWER: **Lots more.** On average seahorses can release between 100 to 1,000 babies – a bit like confetti cannons, only cuter.

3.   **Next is an African driver ant. More or less than the average 100–1,000 of the seahorse?**

ANSWER: **Loads more!** An African driver ant can lay up to four million eggs over the course of around 25 days. Still, not a candle on the sunfish. Or whatever lays those Cadbury's Cream ones.

4.   **And finally – a bluefin tuna? More than an African driver ant? Or less?**

ANSWER: **It's more!** A bluefin tuna can produce 10 million eggs a year. Which is almost as many people as there were in front of me in the queue for Glastonbury last year.

That's the end of **Play Your Clutch Right**, so let's crack on. Not the eggs obviously – that would be awful. I hope you've enjoyed our sideways look at the amazing, massive, sideways egg-laying-champion that is the ocean sunfish. A truly remarkable and wonderfully weird looking fish.

Keeping things beside the seaside, the final animal in this group is one we all know. This is a well-known sea creature with all sorts of funny remarkable habits that have passed us by. Until now. Let's mind the claws as we say hello to the…

Lobster

Living on the bottom of the sea, lobsters are marine crustaceans. They're part of a family of water-living animals – including crabs and shrimps – who are hard-shelled and famous for having several pairs of legs. But less pairs of trainers than me (there are worse afflictions).

Let's talk through some initial lobster facts…

- Lobsters have five pairs of legs. Three of these have claws, including the trademark first pair, which are usually larger than the others.

- There are many different types of lobster – for example, spiny lobsters, squat lobsters and slipper lobsters (famous for their love of wearing tartan slippers). But our focus today is on the lobsters most common in UK waters: the well-known long-clawed lobsters of the family Nephropidae.

- Try saying Nephropidae 100 times in 60 seconds, whilst chewing a Fruit Pastille. I bet you five British pounds you can't (not legally binding).

- Lobsters have long bodies and hard protective exoskeletons, which they regularly shed (once a year for adults). Shedding its exoskeleton enables a lobster to continue growing all its life.

- The average length of a lobster is between 20 and 50cm, but they have been reported as big as 1.2m long! Indeed, Europe's record-breaking lobster, named Leonard, was caught by a diver in Fowey, Cornwall, in 1931. It measured 126cm. That's a whopper lobster! (Thankfully, not yet available at Burger King…)

- We often associate lobsters with being bright red; however, that's the colour they become after being cooked. Lobsters can be many colours, but usually they're dark coloured – dark bluey green or greeny brown. This helps them camouflage with the sea floor and be harder for predators to spot.

How long do lobsters live?

Lobsters can live to an estimated 50 years in the wild. A lobster's age is determined by its continued ability to shed (moult) its skin and grow. Young lobsters can moult five times a year, whilst adults tend to moult once every one to two years. During each moult, the length of a lobster can increase by up to 15 per cent and its weight can double. (Note to self: I must use shedding my exoskeleton as an excuse for my post-Christmas fails on the scales.)

However, moulting can come at a price for lobsters… Creating a new shell takes a vast amount of energy. The larger a lobster becomes, the more energy is required. It's reported that 10 to 15 per cent of lobsters die of exhaustion during moulting (Note to self: I mustn't use shedding my exoskeleton as an excuse for my post-Christmas fails on the scales.)

BONUS LOBSTER AGE FACT:

How do we know that lobsters live to be 50?

A few years back, scientists at the University of New Brunswick in the US, discovered that you can count a lobster's rings to determine its age, in the same way you can count the rings on a tree stump.

Marine biologists already knew they could determine a fish's age by counting the rings in the inner ear, a shark's from the rings in its vertebrae and a clam's from the rings on its shell. But, because lobsters shed their shells, it was thought impossible to figure out a lobster's age in this same way.

However, the New Brunswick team found that lobsters and crabs have two body parts that accumulate rings and never moult: the lobster's eyestalk and a part of the stomach known as 'the gastric mills'. If you take a look at either of these under a microscope, you'll see rings and then deduce the lobster's age.

I don't know about you, but this fact has left me shell-shocked. Come on?! That's actually a proper joke. Okay, I'll get my coat...

How do lobsters get around? Do they use jet skis?

Lobsters don't travel by jet ski (yet). They tend to slowly walk along the sea floor. But they also have strong muscular tails, which can enable them to swim forwards and backwards.

In fact, if a lobster is alarmed, it'll swiftly reverse by quickly curling and uncurling its tail. (Note to self: must try to grow myself a muscular tail.)

How do lobsters eat?

Lobsters eat plants and animal matter. But they don't have teeth like we do. Instead, they chew with their stomachs. I know, you're thinking, 'What the—?! They chew with their stomachs?' Stay with me.

You see, the gastric mill (the part of the stomach I mentioned earlier that helps us determine a lobster's age) is located in the digestive tract. The gastric mill has three grinding surfaces that crush and break down food as it moves from the mouth through the stomach.

Lobsters taste food with their legs!

Based on the fact that chewing occurs in a lobster's stomach, you'd be forgiven for thinking that lobsters aren't fussed with taste or flavour; they just find food, eat it and keep going. But this isn't true: we know that lobsters savour the taste of food with their legs!

Lobsters have the equivalent of taste buds in their front pincers. These taste buds are the hairs on their legs and feet. These chemosensory hairs (sensory nerve endings) identify what the food is and what it tastes like! A bit like when I used to prod my

school mashed potato with a fork and know
immediately that it was going to taste
revolting (well, it's not really like that,
but I'm glad I shared my pain).

And if you think having teeth
in its stomach and taste buds in
its pincers is unusual, did you
know that a lobster's kidneys are
in its head?

> ### BONUS LOBSTER FACT:
>
> I mentioned earlier that lobsters are omnivores. They
> eat most things: including themselves! After they moult,
> lobsters will eat their own shed skin. It turns out that the
> discarded shell is high in calcium, which helps the lobster's
> new shell to harden.
>
> Yummy lobster shell in a lobster's tummy!

'What about lobster sex?' I hear you ask

Copulation... here we are again! I'm glad you asked, because lobster
love is fascinating and funny – as brilliant curator of crustacea at
the Natural History Museum, Miranda Lowe, explained when
she joined us on the show...

Just after shedding her shell, a female lobster releases a
pheromone, letting male lobsters know that she's in the mood.

How does the female release the pheromone?

The simple answer is they pee it out of their faces. The less simple version is that a female lobster waits outside a male's den. She'll then pee in his direction, out of special nozzles on her face. Her urine contains pheromones that let the male know she's ready to reproduce. So, the female's piss pheromone acts as a telegram to male lobsters. The pheromone is saying, 'Come and get me whilst my shell is still soft.'

When a lobster sheds its shell, it's at risk of predation. Thankfully, the released pheromone encourages the male to have sex with the female rather than eat her (remember lobsters aren't fussy eaters and have been known to snack on one another).

So how do lobsters have sex with one another?

The marvellous real answer comes courtesy of Robert C Bayer, from the Lobster Institute at the University of Maine. He's quoted as saying, 'I would describe it as the missionary position.'

So, when it comes to sex, lobsters keep it simple. Nothing too fancy. Perhaps because, rightly or wrongly, the best-selling *Complete Illustrated Karma Sutra* has yet to be translated into shellfish.

Fast forward six to nine months after 'the act' and tiny lobster eggs form on the female lobster's tail. Six to nine months after this, the eggs hatch. Once they've hatched, the lobster larvae float near the surface for four to six weeks. The few that survive (many are eaten by fish) will then settle at the bottom and develop as baby lobsters.

Female lobsters can have approximately 10,000 tiny eggs. The reason they have so many is that very few grow into adults. From every 50,000 eggs, only two lobsters are expected to survive. It's really not easy becoming an adult lobster.

 SUPER BONUS LOBSTER FACT:

Lobsters can regenerate their limbs. It takes between two to five years for a regular lobster to regenerate a lost claw back to its original size, but they can do it.

In 2014, there was the story of a female lobster who was brought into the National Lobster Hatchery in Cornwall. She was laden with eggs but missing both her large front claws and four of her legs. The prospects were bleak. But the female – dubbed 'Clawdia' – surprised staff at the hatchery as she managed to regrow all her limbs and two small – but perfect – new front claws in one moult!

Feeling pain

Scientists have proven that lobsters can – alongside crabs and octopuses – experience pain or discomfort. Lobsters aren't self-aware in the same way we are – they don't tend to have mid-life crises and buy leather jackets – but we know they react to tissue damage and detect pain on some level.

Research has shown that when they're stressed lobsters release a hormone into the bloodstream (cortisol) – the same one that we humans release when we're hurt.

Moreover, when lobsters are put live into a boiling pot they strenuously twitch their tail. As I mentioned earlier, the tail twitch is a lobster's escape reflex. You couldn't get a more visible sign of distress. At the time of writing this I'm still a carnivore. I know I'm a grade-A hypocrite, but learning this fact and writing it down here has affected me.

When you're making comedy (as I've been trying to do for the last 20 years) the accepted rule is to end on a laugh. I appreciate that writing about lobsters feeling pain is a downer. It's interesting, when we record the shows, some of the best bits aren't funny, but get you thinking. I love the fact that the show is a mix: funny stuff and thought-provoking. Light and shade.

On that note, we've just had some shade, so how about we end this section with some light. And by light I mean, let's celebrate fabulous lobsters with some jokes. Here goes…

Q. Why did the lobster giggle?
A. Because the seaweed.

Q. What does every lobster like to drink in the morning?
A. Clawfee.

Q. Did you hear about the lobster that went to a party?
A. It pulled a mussel.

Q. Why was the ocean screaming?
A. You would too if you had a lobster on your bottom.

Remember, comedy is subjective. We all have a different sense of humour and that's okay.

So that's our look at lobsters and this group of creatures beside the sea. Time for an ice-cream methinks.

BITESIZE NATURE TABLE

Before we move on to our next *Nature Table* group of animals, here are some more funsize *Nature Table* facts for you.

Did you know...?

The word 'hippopotamus' comes from the ancient Greek, meaning 'river horse'. So, although they invented democracy, trial by jury and even the indoor shower, this proves the ancient Greeks knew sod all about what horses look like.

Chinese soft-shell turtles urinate through their mouths – just one of many reasons I regret kissing that Chinese soft-shell turtle.

The word 'capercaillie' comes from the Gaelic meaning 'horse of the woods'. This proves that at least the ancient Greeks weren't the worst at knowing what horses looked like.

The titan arum plant grows over 10m high and has the odour of a rotting corpse – which apparently makes it, and I quote, 'an inappropriate Mother's Day gift'.

THE WILD GIANTS

This final group of the book is big on size, in all its guises. Everything we're looking at here has a scintillating size-y story to tell.

So, without further ado – or indeed any ado (seriously, what is 'ado'?) – let's check out this group... The Wild Giants.

Let's meet our first contestant. Who are you and where are you from?

Bush Cricket

Living in southern Europe, there's a species of bush cricket, *Platycleis affinis*, that has record-breaking testicles. Aren't you pleased you bought this book?

Top entomologist Dr Karim Vahed joined us on the show to inform us that this specific bush cricket – which is 3cm in length – has baked bean-sized testicles. And we're off...

Karim informed us that bush cricket balls are the world's largest testicles of any internally fertilising species, relative to its body mass. Put simply, this bush cricket's balls account for 14 per cent of its total body weight, making them record holding balls. This 14 per cent is roughly equivalent to a human man walking around with tyre-sized testicles, weighing approximately 5kg each. For context, an adult cat is 5kg. That's right, I'm saying it's like a human walking around with testicles the size of adult cats. Clearly male bush crickets must have incredibly strong legs.

But who has the actual largest testicles in the world?

I thought you might ask. Although this bush cricket's testicles are record-breaking, they're not the largest balls on the planet. This prize belongs to the right whale, a large mammal that's generally between 13 and 16m long and weighing up to 70 tonnes. A right whale's testicles are about the size of a small family hatchback: a Seat Ibiza or Ford Focus. If I'm honest, the brand of car has no consequence. But as big as the right whale's balls are, they're only 1 per cent of the mammal's total body weight. So, the bush cricket wins when we consider the size of the testicles in relation to body mass.

So how come male bush crickets have such big plums?

The size of male bush cricket genitalia stems from the fact that female bush crickets are polyamorous and promiscuous; the females mate with many males. Scientists have hypothesised that by having bigger testes, a male bush cricket can win the war to have their progeny succeed.

As Karim explained, there's a strong-held belief that by having large testicles, the bush cricket has large reserves of sperm. If it releases a small amount of these sperm into several females, the male is boosting its chances of reproductive success. Karim also shared a second theory: large testes means you have a lot in the barrel (as it were). In turn, this might help any male bush crickets who are 'firing blanks'.

But there's more to the bush cricket's reproductive story...

Karim let us know that female bush crickets are super canny and most impressive when it comes to reproduction. The males have big balls but, in reality, it's the females who are calling the shots.

You see, a female bush cricket has an expandable sperm sack. This sack enables the female to store the sperm of all the bush crickets she's mated with. As a result, females can choose which specific sperm to reproduce with. So, no matter how well-endowed the males may be, the females determine which sperm they want to go with.

Linked to this, female bush crickets will avoid mating with the same male, choosing instead to mate with multiple males. Studies have shown that mating with multiple partners can improve hatching success and survival of the offspring. Put simply: the more males you mate with, the more chance you have of securing grade-A sperm with better-suited genes. Clearly, female bush crickets are savvy when it comes to reproduction – not putting all their eggs in one basket!

BONUS SEXY BUSH CRICKET FACT:

Did you know that male bush crickets sexually arouse females using vibrators? You didn't? I suggest you read on...

I say the males use 'vibrators'. In the science community the official term is 'titillators'. 'Titillators' sounds much more serious and grown up... Anyway, male bush crickets have a pair of curved rods – or titillators – that point out of their genital openings. The titillators look a bit like coat hooks.

Using CT scans (a computer X-ray that can obtain detailed internal images of the body), German scientists have studied bush crickets as they're mating. It's a tough job, but someone has to do it. The scientists have discovered that, during sex, a male bush cricket will rhythmically insert his titillators into the female's genital opening. The male's titillators tap on a plate covered in sensory cells inside the female's genitals. It's believed that the titillators help the male keep the female sexually interested. No, I'm not making this up.

Not much more I can add to this. Thank you, scientists, for putting bush crickets under a CT scan and watching them have sex, so that I can share this with readers.

So now you're enlightened to the wild sex lives of giant testicled bush crickets, how about we play a game? No, not one of those games.

Did you know that bush crickets (and in fact all crickets) have their ears on their knees? If they're anything like me, it means

they'd be deafened by creaks every time they got out of bed in the morning. So, how about we explore other misplaced body parts of the animal kingdom, as we play the catchily titled game...
Heads on Tails!

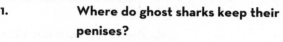

1.   **Where do ghost sharks keep their penises?**
        (a) on their tails
        (b) on their heads
        (c) nowhere, ghosts don't have genitals, stupid!!!

ANSWER: **It's b – ghost sharks have their penises on their heads.** No giggling at the back; this is science.

2.   **Right, second question – where are a giant clam's eyes?**
        (a) on its shell
        (b) on its body
        (c) nowhere, a giant clam doesn't have eyes

ANSWER: **It's b again – giant clams have several hundred, pinhole-like eyes that line the exposed exterior of their body.** These structures sense light and allow the giant clam to perceive nearby predators. If a giant clam senses a predator, it can retract back into its shell, and cause water to jet out quickly to scare off the enemy. Scaring a predator with a natural water pistol: clever clam I say!

3. **Next... a tuatara is a scaly, lizard-like reptile. But what does it have on its forehead?**
(a) one giant antenna
(b) the penis of a ghost shark
(c) a third eye

ANSWER: **It's c – the tuatara has a third eye in its forehead.** It's only visible in the hatchlings and its purpose is unknown. Unless its purpose is 'freaking me out'. In which case, done.

4. **And finally... where do you think a nudibranch marine mollusc breathes from?**

(a) its gills

(b) its snorkel

(c) its anus

ANSWER **It's c – the nudibranch breathes through its anus, which, thinking about it, might just be its polite way of saying it farts a lot.**

So, that's big-balled bush crickets. I hope you've enjoyed saying hello to these splendid, well-endowed, promiscuous and, dare I say it, kinky crickets.

Our next big-on-size creature is an arthropod that you could never accuse of being legless (no matter how many glasses of prosecco it has drunk)...

Giant Centipede

Aka the Peruvian giant yellow-leg centipede, the giant centipede is the largest centipede in the world. Giant centipedes can exceed 30cm in length and tend to live in the moist, dark rainforests of South America and the southern Caribbean. Typically, they can live for about ten years.

Giant centipedes are uncompromising carnivores, feeding on any other animal they can overpower and kill. Not only can these centipedes overcome worms, snails and scorpions, but – thanks to their size – they also take on tarantulas, snakes, mice – and even bats!

How does a centipede hunt a bat?

When it comes to bats, giant centipedes are fiendish, daredevil hunters. They'll climb onto a cave's ceiling and with only a few legs holding them to the ceiling, they'll clasp onto a heavy perching bat until it's dead.

Amazingly, Amazonian giant centipedes can even catch and kill flying bats mid-air by hanging from the ceiling and grabbing a bat mid-flight. I often have trouble skewering a pea on my plate.

BONUS GIANT CENTIPEDE FACT:

Not only can giant centipedes hunt flying prey - like bats - but we now know they can also follow prey into water.

Some giant centipedes have been seen swimming in fresh water. The *Scolopendra cataracta* has been spotted in Laos, Thailand and Vietnam. It grows up to 20cm, has a really nasty bite and can swim! Maybe switch your holiday to Oxford next year?

How do giant centipedes kill their prey? Do they tap-dance them to death?

The giant centipede's main weapon is its venom. It transfers this venom by biting its prey. The venom sacks are just behind the head and they use their modified front legs to pierce the prey and inject the venom.

When natural history presenter and author Martin Hughes-Games joined us on the show, he claimed that one of the most painful bites in the world is from the giant centipede. Martin told us about an extraordinary encounter he had in the US...

A few years back, Martin was fronting a TV wildlife documentary in North America. During filming, he went to interview Major Scott Stockwell of the US Army, who happens to be a scorpion expert.

When they first met, Scott pulled out a giant centipede from his collection. The centipede immediately dug its fangs into the major's hand and started pumping in venom. According to Martin, Scott's hand started dramatically puffing up, like someone blowing into a rubber washing up glove!

Martin was concerned that the man might die from the giant caterpillar's venom (it's rare, but very occasionally people have died). Martin asked, 'Shall I call an ambulance?' To which Major Stockwell calmly replied, 'Let's go to lunch!' Thinking this was weird – but going along with it – Martin drove them both to a restaurant. All the while, as they drove, the major's hand continued to swell more and more.

It transpired Scott knew that the poison wouldn't kill him and he chose to play an eccentric game of 'mind over matter' whilst tucking into his lunch. Somehow, Major Stockwell was able to control the pain in his mind. The pair of them had lunch, the pain eventually subsided and that was that. Martin drove the major back and they finished filming. Quite extraordinary.

Author's health and safety tip:
I'd like to suggest that if you're unfortunate enough to be bitten by a giant centipede, I wouldn't make my first port of a call a diner. No matter how good the loaded fries are, I recommend you get yourself to A&E first. **Always remember:** A&E first, then loaded fries.

> **★ SUPER BONUS GIANT CENTIPEDE FACTS:**
>
> Thanks to their many legs, giant centipedes can move very fast. In fact they can walk 0.4m per second (about a quarter of the speed of an Olympic swimmer – obviously when an Olympic swimmer is swimming. Not dancing).
>
> And on the subject of the giant centipede's legs, did you know that each pair of feet is slightly longer than the one in front? I assume so the centipede never trips itself up!

So you now know that the giant centipede's bite can be bad. But how bad exactly, compared to other insect attacks? Let's see if you can figure out what's 'higher or lower' in terms of pain with a round of the ratings classic… **Play Your Bites Right!**

To play this, we'll be measuring the strength and severity of an insect's sting on the Schmidt pain index, comparing each sting with the one before. This pain scale was devised by entomologist Justin Schmidt, the 'King of Sting', who has had the unfortunate experience of being stung by so many insects that he created his very own pain scale, ranging from bites at Level 1 all the way up to the excruciating Level 4.

I would say fingers on buzzers, but that's how you get stung in the first place.

According to the Schmidt pain scale, the giant centipede is at the top of his pain scale at Level 4.

1.   **So, starting with the giant sweat bee, do you think that's at the same level, or lower than the giant centipede?**

ANSWER: **The answer is lower!** The giant sweat bee sting is a modest 1.5 on the scale. Schmidt describes it thus: 'a silver tablespoon drops squarely on your toe, sending you hopping.'

2.   **Next – higher or lower than the sweat bee: the western yellowjacket wasp?**

ANSWER: **It's higher!** The western yellowjacket
           sounds like something you'd wear to a
           barn dance but it's a wasp with a Level
           2 sting. Schmidt describes the pain
           as 'hot and smoky, almost irreverent.
           Imagine W.C. Fields extinguishing a
           cigar on your tongue.'

3.   **How about this one? The warrior
           wasp? Higher or lower than the
           western yellowjacket?**

ANSWER: **The warrior wasp is higher,** at a
           staggering 4 on the scale. Schmidt says:
           'Torture. You are chained in the flow of
           an active volcano. Why did I start this
           list?'

4.   **Next – the bullet ant. Is that higher or
           lower than the warrior wasp?**

ANSWER: **Bit of a trick question as they're pretty
           much level pegging.** They're both at the
           top at Level 4, so it depends which type
           of pain you prefer: 'walking over flaming
           charcoal with a 7.5cm nail embedded in
           your heel' or 'a running hair dryer has

been dropped into your bubble bath. Lie down and scream.' But the latter – the bullet ant sting pain – lasts longer, around five hours.

5.   **Next up: a group of guests not leaving your party for several hours when you're already yawning and hinting that it's time to call it a day. Higher or lower than the warrior wasp?**

ANSWER: **There is nothing more irritating than that, so they are definitely higher.**

6.   **And finally, higher or lower than the party guests: the ferocious polybia wasp?**

ANSWER: **It's lower**. The ferocious polybia wasp only feels like, and I quote, 'your posterior is a target for a BB gun. Bullseye, over and over.' Not exactly tempting but certainly not living up to its name.

And that's the end of **Play Your Bites Right** – for the winner, this massive tube of Savlon. Oh sorry, it's run out.

Our next creature is perhaps a surprising addition to the wild giants group. It's not a creature immediately identified by its record-breaking size. But then that's what makes nature so cool: it loves to surprise us.

Let's put our goggles and flippers on and swim hundreds of miles into the ocean (or maybe it's just easier to get a speedboat), dive down into the blue and hopefully spot us some...

Barnacles

Living in the sea, barnacles are small sticky crustaceans with hard external shells. Related to lobsters and crabs, barnacles are one of the oldest living animals in the world. They can range in size from less than 1.5–15cm in diameter. I appreciate this doesn't sound especially 'wild giant' but please trust me: barnacles are giants. They're size-y in a most peculiar way. We'll get to that shortly.

There are approximately 1,000 different species of barnacles that we know about. What makes them stand out from other arthropods (invertebrates with multiple joints and an exoskeleton), is they're sessile (they don't move about). Living inside a shell, barnacles attach themselves to a hard surface, be that a rock, a ship, a sea turtle or even a whale.

If you're not sure what barnacles look like, when you see a photo or film of a humpback whale, you'll often see clusters of nobbly bits on the whale's body; often around the throat or tail. These nobbles are colonies of barnacle shells attached to the whale's skin (whales often have around 200 barnacles across their bodies). Inside each shell lives a barnacle: a weird creature that looks a bit prawn-like. You'll be pleased to hear that barnacles don't harm the whale they're attached to, they're just there hitching a ride.

How do barnacles attach themselves to a hard surface?

Barnacles produce a cement-like substance that welds them to a solid surface for life, so they really do have to choose between a rock and a hard place! I'm sorry. Time again for me to get my coat...

BONUS BARNACLE FACT:

Did you know that barnacles eat with their legs? And before you ask, it's not because they have awful table manners. There's a legit evolutionary reason for eating with their legs. Since barnacles aren't fussed about being able to move, their legs have adapted, over time, to have a different use...

Barnacles use their legs to comb the sea and capture tiny food, like plankton. A barnacle's legs then pass this food to their mouth parts. This is a wonderfully effective way of eating, yet barnacles somehow still manage to get mustard on their T-shirts.

If barnacles are only a few inches in diameter, how come you've put them in a group called Wild Giants?

Very good question! The very awesome and joyous Miranda Lowe, the Natural History Museum's principal curator of crustacea, explained all when she came on the show…

Barnacles are worthy members of the wild giant club because they have (drumroll please)…

The longest penis relative to body size in the entire animal kingdom.

Boom! Put that fact in your pipe and smoke it.

Some barnacles have penises that extend eight times the length of their bodies. And so you know, we haven't just taken male barnacles' word for it. This fact has been scientifically verified. Which is just as well, because male barnacles are notorious for exaggerating.

Why does a barnacle need a big wiener?

Picture a barnacle. It's stuck to a rock or a whale. It can't move. It wants to reproduce and – as we all know – finding a date can be difficult in today's world. There are no dating apps for barnacles. plentyofbarnacles.com isn't a thing.

Over there in the corner, fixed to a different rock, our barnacle spots another barnacle. Our barnacle can't just shuffle over to the second and say hello. As you know, barnacles are fixed to one spot and only use their legs for eating.

So, to solve this problem, barnacles have evolved to grow themselves a giant penis that can reach other barnacles and fertilise their eggs. And that's why a barnacle has a penis EIGHT TIMES its body length!

Barnacle sex

I know you're wondering, so here's how barnacles have sex, as explained to us by the wonderful Miranda Lowe...

The barnacle's penis exits the shell and starts the hunt for another barnacle to mate with. To help find a receptive barnacle, barnacles' penises have evolved to be able to smell and taste. Yep, barnacle penises are multi-skilled.

Once the barnacle's giant penis finds another willing barnacle, it delivers sperm to the eggs and fertilises them. The barnacle then protects the eggs until they hatch.

★ **SUPER BONUS BARNACLE FACT:**

Did you know that Charles Darwin was obsessed with barnacles?

Celebrated beard-operator Charles Darwin spent eight years dissecting and describing barnacles. He wrote four large volumes on barnacles: two on recent barnacles and two on fossilised barnacles. I can exclusively reveal that they're currently being adapted by Netflix. *The Barnacle Identity*, starring Matt Damon as... Jason Barnacle. What's so great about this book is the vast number of fascinating exclusives.

So, you now know that barnacles have the longest penis of any animal – relative to its body size. It's up to eight times the barnacle's length, as they won't stop telling us. But in terms of ratios, is anything else in the natural world as out of proportion as a barnacle's appendage? Methinks it's time for a round of the popular teatime gameshow, **It's All Relative!**

I'm going to fire a series of relative statements at you and you have to work out if they're true or false.

1.   **So, for our opener: A chameleon's tongue is the same length as its body? Is that true or false?**

ANSWER: **That's false.** The chameleon's tongue is actually twice as long as its body. So, if you're sitting in your house and you just see a giant pink disembodied tongue, you've got a chameleon problem.

2.   **Next one: the tarsier, a primate found in the islands of Southeast Asia, has eyes that make up around 16 per cent of its body. Is that true or false?**

ANSWER: **That's true.** The tarsier is the mammal with the largest eyes in proportion to its body. Each eye is larger than its brain. So, while they're exceedingly cute, they're absolutely no use on a pub quiz team.

3. How about the *T-rex*? Back when *T-rexes* roamed, their arms were one thirteenth the length of their bodies? True or false?

ANSWER: **That's true!** Adult *T-rexes* were around 12m long, though the arms were less than 1m. They looked out of proportion, but there's no way I'm telling them that.

4. And finally: the brain of a bony-eared assfish is less than one thousandth of its total mass. Is that true or did we just make it up?

ANSWER: **That's absolutely true.** The bony-eared assfish exists – hurray for that. Researchers found one that weighed 40g, with a brain weighing less than 30mg. Even the author of this book (that's me) doesn't have that brain-to-body-mass ratio – and that's saying something. Or maybe it comes as no surprise!

So, that's the end of the game and our look at the world of the wild giants. It's also the end of this book. What a finale! The bush cricket, the giant centipede and the barnacle; a wonderfully eclectic group. It turns out that to be a colossus of the animal kingdom, you can be all sorts of shapes and sizes. What a lovely way to finish.

Right, where's my limousine? I'm supposed to be doing a voiceover for Big Al's Ranch in an hour.

Epilogue

So, that's it. That's apparently what people in the know refer to as 'a book'.

I hope you've enjoyed reading it. It's been a lot of fun for me revisiting many of the different flora and fauna we've learned about and giggled at across the series.

We all know we're at a crux right now with our planet. I hope in its own silly way, this book highlights what's at stake and reminds you WHY the fight to save our planet is so important.

Our natural kingdom is a jaw-droppingly, incredible, beautiful, phenomenal (and funny) thing. It's been around longer than us and it will continue way after we obliterate ourselves in some dumb self-destructive way. There is so much we can learn from — and indeed chuckle at — the natural world.

If any of the facts in this book have moved or entertained you, please spread the word. Share the facts with your friends. The more we get this stuff out there, the more we can educate, amuse and maybe change people's mindsets.

It's important to care. And it's important to laugh.

I'd like to end this book with a quote. I could end it with film critic Leslie Halliwell's review of Charles Bronson's 1982 action thriller, *Deathwish II*...

'Bad art is one thing, but this is ridiculous.'

But I think that might denigrate what we've done here. Better, I think, to end with this quote. I think it's lovely, it's hopeful, and for whatever reason just feels apt to me...

'It never hurts to keep looking for sunshine.'

A.A. Milne

Acknowledgements

In putting this book together, the biggest thank you in the universe must go to all the brilliant guests who have appeared on *Nature Table*, sharing their amazing wildlife facts with us. Without our experts and comedian guests, we wouldn't have a show or indeed this book. And on that note, an equally big universe-sized thank you must also go to the natural world itself. Thank you for giving us an unlimited supply of jaw-dropping facts and big laughs. Natural world, you rock!

Making *Nature Table* is a team effort and we're lucky to have such an awesome team. I want to give a big thank you to the best writing, research and production team in the world...

Thank you to our excellent writers, Jon Hunter, Catherine Brinkworth, Kat Sadler, Jenny Laville and Nicky Roberts. Thank you also to our brilliant researcher Catherine Beazley who gives the writers source material to write silly jokes and build games around (some of which appear here). Big up to our ace production team Sarah Nicholls, Mabel Wright, Richard Morris and – of course – recording engineer and editor extraordinaire, Mr Jerry Peal. Thank you also to the supportive grown-ups at BBC Radio 4: our commissioners, first Sioned Wiliam now Julia McKenzie, and le grand fromage Mohit Bakaya who continue to allow us to make the shows. Thank you Team *Nature Table*!

Big high five to Joe Hallsworth, my editor on this book. Your feedback and notes have been so helpful and your cheery can-do approach has made this such fun to work on. And to my agent Vivienne Clore, who is very good at telling me to stop overthinking everything and just get on with it... thank you. You're ace.

And finally, to the very best host in the world, Susan of the Perkins. Thank you so much for meeting me for a coffee in 2019 and agreeing to front this bonkers idea. You have a ludicrously brilliant comic brain, alongside a warm encouraging manner that gives the shows their heart as well as laughs. You bring out the best in our guests and for that I am so grateful.

Thank you Perks for leading from the front, making *Nature Table* the joyous, warm, silly thing that it is.